The pla

HARPER
TO KILL A MO

The play of
HARPER LEE'S
TO KILL A
MOCKINGBIRD

by
Christopher Sergel

Heinemann Educational Books

Heinemann Educational Books Ltd
Halley Court, Jordan Hill, Oxford OX2 8EJ

OXFORD LONDON EDINBURGH
MADRID ATHENS BOLOGNA PARIS
MELBOURNE SYDNEY AUCKLAND
IBADAN NAIROBI HARARE GABORONE
SINGAPORE TOKYO PORTSMOUTH NH (USA)

Printed in England by Clays Ltd, St Ives plc

CONTENTS

Introduction

In an interview Harper Lee gave to *Newsweek* following the publication and huge popular success of her novel, *To Kill a Mockingbird*, she was asked about the writers she most admired. She expressed a particular regard for Jane Austen – 'writing, cameo-like, in that little corner of the world of hers and making it universal'. She could well have been talking about herself for Harper Lee has made Maycomb, 'an epic canvas against which is enacted a lovingly human drama of the jostling worlds – of children and adults, of innocence and experience, of kindness and cruelty, of love and hatred, of humour and pathos, and above all of appearance and reality – all taking the reader to the root of human behaviour' (R. A. Dave, *Harper Lee's Tragic Vision*, 1974).

I believe that Christopher Sergel's dramatisation similarly takes a theatre audience 'to the root of human behaviour'. When the novel was first published, reviewers said it was, 'an insight into Southern mores' and 'a compassionate, deeply moving ... most persuasive plea for racial justice'. They also recognised the 'strong contemporary ... significance' of the work. In his play, Christopher Sergel has shifted the focus slightly, away from the 'Southern mores' (Part One of the novel explores the social background in great detail) and towards what is the novel's central theme – the tragedy of Tom Robinson and of race relations in the 'deep south'. The result of this shift, I believe, highlights the novel's universal qualities. It remains a plea for racial justice and tolerance, but Sergel has managed to bring it closer to home. What Christoher Sergel reminds us, in this play, is that the issues explored are not those of a 'regional' work of art (as the novel is often categorised), but are of importance in Nottingham, Manchester, Birmingham or wherever the play is seen by an audience.

Nelle Harper Lee was born on April 28th, 1926, the youngest of three children born to Amasa Coleman Lee, a lawyer, and

Frances Finch Lee. She attended the local school in the small town of Monroeville, Alabama and from there went in 1944 to Huntingdon College, Montgomery for a year. From 1945 until 1949, she was a student at the University of Alabama, studying law, and spent one of those years as an exchange student at Oxford University. Six months before completing her degree, she left the University to live in New York and write. She supported herself in New York by working as an airline reservations clerk, and eventually approached a literary agent with two essays and three short stories. The agent saw the potential in one of the stories and encouraged Harper Lee to develop it into a novel. She gave up her job in order to concentrate on this work. By this time her father had become ill, and she had to divide her time between New York and Monroeville.

The first manuscript of *To Kill a Mockingbird* was submitted to a publisher in 1957. Although the publisher thought it a promising piece of work, 'it seemed to be a series of short stories strung together'. He suggested that she re-write it. With the help of an editor, Tay Hohoff, she revised the novel and it was finally published in 1960.

To Kill a Mockingbird was an immediate success: selected by the Literary Guild for distribution, recommended by the Book of the Month Club and issued in an abridged version by *Reader's Digest*. In 1961, it won the Pulitzer Prize for fiction, and the Brotherhood Award of the National Conference of Christians and Jews. In the following year, it won the Paperback of the Year Award and was filmed, (the film itself won an Academy Award). Apart from one or two magazine articles, Harper Lee has published no other work, although she has said she has a novel in preparation.

Ray Speakman

BIBLIOGRAPHY

There are few critical works which deal specifically with Harper Lee's *To Kill a Mockingbird*. They include:

R. A. Dave, *Harper Lee's Tragic Vision* (1974);
Rosamund Metcalf, *To Kill a Mockingbird* (York Notes Series), a particularly thorough work.

For useful background information, see:

Malcolm Bradbury and Howard Temperley, *Introduction to American Studies* (Longman, 1981);
Marshall Walker, *The Literature of the United States of America* (Macmillan, 1983).

For works which deal with some of the issues handled in the play, see:

Challenges and *Choices* (Heinemann Educational Books, 1986).

Both works contain plays and follow-up material which touches upon similar issues, and the notes may provide additional help and suggestions.

Buddy, the play – and novel – by Nigel Hinton (Heinemann Educational Books, 1987).

Buddy has a Boo Radley-like character who might offer the opportunity for interesting comparisons.

For support beyond these works, consult:

The English Curriculum: Race and *The English Curriculum: Gender* (The English Centre, Sutherland Street, London SW1).

TO KILL A MOCKINGBIRD

CHARACTERS

'SCOUT' FINCH	A young girl; her hair is plain and she wears dungarees.
JEAN LOUISE FINCH	'Scout' grown older; she wears simple modern clothes.
JEM FINCH	Scout's brother; an active boy, a few years older than her.
ATTICUS FINCH	Their father; he is a tall, quietly impressive, 'civilised' man of nearly fifty. He wears glasses because of poor sight in his left eye and looks with his right when he wants to see something well. He acts as defence counsel for Tom Robinson.
CALPURNIA	The black housekeeper who has helped to bring up Scout and Jem since their mother died.
DILL	Friend of Scout and Jem. He is a little older than Scout and is small, blond and wise. He is neat, well-dressed with an undercurrent of sophistication, but his laugh is sudden and happy.
MISS MAUDIE ATKINSON	A sympathetic neighbour.
MISS STEPHANIE CRAWFORD	The neighbourhood scold.

MRS DUBOSE	An elderly and bad-tempered neighbour; she supports herself with a stick.
MR CUNNINGHAM	A farmer and client of Atticus Finch.
MAYELLA EWELL	A poor girl of nineteen, accustomed to strenuous labour, who accuses Tom Robinson of attacking her.
BOB EWELL	Her father; a little 'bantam cock' of a man. He is ignorant and sharp-tempered.
MR GILMER	The counsel for the prosecution in the trial of Tom Robinson.
NATHAN RADLEY	A pale, thin, leathery man; 'Boo' Radley's older brother and guardian.
ARTHUR 'BOO' RADLEY	A mysterious, tall figure; pale, nervous and withdrawn.
TOM ROBINSON	A powerful, young black man, but with his left hand curled up and held to his chest.
HELEN ROBINSON	His wife.
REVEREND SYKES	A black minister, conservatively dressed in a black suit, white shirt and black tie.
HECK TATE	The sheriff.
JUDGE TAYLOR	The judge who tries the case of Tom Robinson.
COURT CLERK	
THE MOB	A group of men dressed in farm clothes.

ACT ONE

(*The houselights dim and in the darkness there are the soft sounds of birds, and in the distance, a dog barking.*

The stage light comes up, revealing a girl who is now sitting in the porch swing, thoughtfully swinging back and forth. Her hair is plain and she wears dungarees.

A woman, dressed in simple modern clothes, comes on stage. If possible, there should be something about her that suggests the girl-in-the-swing, grown older, for this is who she is. The woman, Jean Louise Finch, was called 'Scout' when she was young, and so the young girl in the swing will be called SCOUT, while the same person, grown older, is called JEAN.

JEAN is looking about as though seeing this place in memory. As she comes up to the tree, she reaches up and touches a place on the trunk. She is smiling as she speaks, softly to herself.)

JEAN: The cement would still be there covering the knothole.

(*A voice is heard calling from offstage. It is the voice of CALPURNIA.*)

CALPURNIA (*calling*): Scout – where are you? Scout, you come here.

JEAN: My name is Jean Louise, but when I was that young girl there on the swing ... they called me 'Scout'.

1

CALPURNIA: You hear me, Scout?

SCOUT (*still swinging; preoccupied*): I'm watching for Atticus.

JEAN: Atticus – that's my father. Back then he seemed ancient ... feeble. He was a lawyer and nearly fifty. When my brother Jem asked him why he was so old, he said he got started late – which we thought reflected on his manliness. He was much older than the parents of our school contemporaries and there was nothing Jem or I could say about him.

SCOUT (*speaking forward*): Because he doesn't do anything. Atticus doesn't drive a dump truck for the county, he isn't a sheriff, he doesn't farm, or work in a garage, or anything worth mentioning. *Other* fathers go hunting, play poker, or fish. Atticus works in an office, and he reads.

JEAN: With those attributes, however, Atticus did not remain as inconspicuous as Jem and I might have wished. (*With feeling*) No, he did not! .

BOY'S VOICE (*calling from offstage*): Hey, Scout – how come your daddy defends niggers? (*Singsong*) Scout's daddy defends nig ... gers!

(SCOUT *has risen and comes to the porch railing, her fists clenched.*)

SCOUT: You gonna take that back, boy?

BOY'S VOICE: You gonna make me? My folks say your daddy's a disgrace and that nigger oughta hang from the water tank.

SCOUT: You take that back!

BOY'S VOICE (*going away*): Make me! Try and make me!

CALPURNIA (*voice offstage*): Scout. I've told you to come in.

SCOUT: I'm not ready to come in. (*Going back to the swing*) I have to talk to Atticus.

JEAN: It was Maycomb, Alabama and it was back in 1935 when I was that girl – back when ugly words were first shouted at us – back at the beginning of an experience that brought a man to his death. (*Looking towards the house*) And it brought Boo Radley storming out of that shut-up house – the attack on me – Jem's arm broken – another man killed! (*Turning back towards the front of the stage*) But that isn't what I want to remember. That's not why my mind's come back here. (*Trying to sort this out*) There's something I have to do – something my father wanted. Probably enough years have gone by – enough so I can look back – perhaps even enough so now I can do the one thing my father asked. (*Correcting herself with a smile; almost as an afterthought*) No – there was one other thing. When he gave us air rifles, he asked us never to kill a mockingbird.

(MISS MAUDIE ATKINSON *has come out onto her porch.*)

MISS MAUDIE (*to* JEAN LOUISE): Your father's right. Mocking-birds just make music. They don't eat up people's gardens, don't nest in corncribs; they don't do one thing but sing their hearts out. That's why it's a sin to kill a mockingbird.

SCOUT (*crossing to the porch rail*): Miss Maudie – this is an old neighbourhood, ain't it?

MISS MAUDIE (*turning toward* SCOUT): Been here longer than the town.

SCOUT: No, I mean the folks on our street are all old. Jem and me's the only children. Mrs Dubose is close on a hundred and Miss Crawford's old and so are you and Atticus.

MISS MAUDIE (*tartly*): Not being wheeled around yet. Neither's your father. You're lucky. You and Jem have the benefit of your father's age. If your father was thirty, you'd find life quite different.

SCOUT (*emphatically*): I sure would. Atticus can't do anything.

MISS MAUDIE: You'd be surprised. There's life in him yet.

SCOUT: *What* can he do?

MISS MAUDIE: Quite a lot. (*As she goes*) Seems to me you'd be proud of him.

SCOUT (*calling after her; concerned*): Why? The way some

3

folks are starting to go on, you'd think he was running a still.

(*Realising Miss Maudie is gone,* SCOUT *returns to the swing.*)

SCOUT: I have to speak to him.

JEAN: We lived over there – Atticus, my brother Jem, and Calpurnia, our cook, who raised us. Calpurnia was all angles and bones.

(CALPURNIA *has come out onto the porch.*)

CALPURNIA: You come in and wash up before your father gets home.

SCOUT (*rising, but under protest*): I said I wasn't ready.

CALPURNIA: Your brother's already washed. Why don't you behave as well as Jem?

SCOUT: Because he's older than me and you know it.

CALPURNIA (*giving her a smack to encourage her along*): Get in there.

(*They both go into the house.*)

JEAN: Calpurnia's hand was as hard as a bed slat. My mother died when I was two, so I never felt her absence. (*Smiling wryly*) But I felt Calpurnia's tyrannical presence as long as I could remember.

SCOUT (*voice, from inside the house*): The water's too hot.

CALPURNIA (*voice, also from inside the house; unimpressed*): Keep scrubbin'!

JEAN (*considering the neighbourhood*): Even in 1935, Maycomb, Alabama was already a tired old town.

(HECK TATE *and* JUDGE TAYLOR *enter.*)

JEAN (*continuing*): In rainy weather the streets turned to red slop; grass grew on the sidewalks, the courthouse sagged in the square. (*Noticing them*) That's Heck Tate – the sheriff, and Judge Taylor.

HECK (*calling*): Atticus – you home?

(CALPURNIA *comes out onto the porch.*)

CALPURNIA: Not yet, Mr Tate. Afternoon, Judge Taylor.
HECK: Cal – tell him we were passing by.

(*They nod and start to go.*)

CALPURNIA: You want him to call?
JUDGE (*as they go; pleasantly*): We'll be seeing him anyway.

(CALPURNIA *re-enters the house, and* MISS STEPHANIE CRAW-FORD *comes on.*)

JEAN: People moved slowly then – and somehow it was hotter. A day was twenty-four hours long, but seemed longer. There was no hurry for there was nowhere to go, nothing to buy and no money to buy it with.

(MISS STEPHANIE *has paused to consider the house with disapproval.*)

MISS STEPHANIE: Lack of money is no excuse to let a place go like that. At the least they could cut the Johnson grass and rabbit-tobacco. (*She turns toward* JEAN) But of course, they're Radleys.
JEAN (*identifying her*): Miss Stephanie Crawford – a neighbourhood scold. According to her, everybody in Maycomb has a streak: a drinking streak, a gambling streak, a mean streak, a funny streak.
MISS STEPHANIE (*emphatically*): No Atkinson minds his own business; every third Merriweather is morbid; the truth is

5

not in the Delafields; all the Bufords walk like that; if Mrs Grace sips gin out of Lydia E. Pinkham bottles, it is nothing unusual – her mother did the same.

JEAN: She was also your principal source of information about Boo Radley.

MISS STEPHANIE (*coming closer; speaking confidentially and with relish*): When that boy was in his teens, he took up with some bad ones from Old Sarum. They were arrested on charges of disorderly conduct, disturbing the peace, assault and battery, and using abusive and profane language in the presence and hearing of a female. Boo Radley was released to his father, who shut him up in that house, and he wasn't seen again for fifteen years.

JEAN: I'd have to ask – as she intended. (*To her*) Miss Stephanie, what happened fifteen years later?

MISS STEPHANIE (*delighted to continue*): Boo Radley was sitting in the living room cutting some items from *The Maycomb Tribune* to paste in his scrapbook. As his father passed by, Boo drove the scissors into his parent's leg, pulled them out, wiped them on his pants and resumed his activities. Boo was then thirty-three. Mr Radley said no Radley was going to any insane asylum. So he was kept home, where he is till this day.

JEAN: How do you know? How can you be sure he's still there?

MISS STEPHANIE (*as she goes into her house; emphatically*): Because I haven't seen him carried out yet.

(MISS STEPHANIE *exits.*)

JEAN (*regarding the Radley house*): Jem and I had never seen him. That didn't come till later, and when it did, we were in no condition to take much notice, being in fear for our lives!

(JEAN *turns back toward the audience.*)

Act I

JEAN: People said Boo Radley went out at night when the moon was down. When azaleas froze in a cold snap, it was because he breathed on them. The tall Radley pecan trees shook their fruit into the adjoining schoolyard in the back, but the nuts lay untouched. Radley pecans would kill you. A baseball hit into the Radley yard was a lost ball and no questions asked.

(*During this,* MRS DUBOSE *has come out onto her porch. She is old and bad-tempered. Supporting herself [partially] with a cane, she crosses to her porch chair which is draped in shawls.* JEM, *an active boy a few years older than* SCOUT, *comes out onto the porch, holding a football.*)

JEAN: My brother Jem – before the fight when his arm got broken.

(JEM *tucks the football under his arm, plunges off the porch, and starts dodging imaginary tacklers.* JEAN *smiles.*)

JEAN: Alabama must be playing in the Rose Bowl with Jem scoring the winning touchdown.

MRS DUBOSE (*sharply*): Where are you going this time of day, Jeremy Finch? Playing hooky, I suppose. I'll just call up the principal and tell him.

JEM: Aw, it's Saturday, Mrs Dubose.

MRS DUBOSE: I wonder if your father knows where you are?

JEM: 'Course he does.

MRS DUBOSE: Maudie Atkinson told me you broke down her scuppernong arbour this morning. She's going to tell your father and then you'll wish you'd never seen the light of day!

JEM (*indignant*): I haven't been near her scuppernong arbour!

MRS DUBOSE: Don't you contradict me!

(JEM *clutches the football as though plunging through centre and, with* MRS DUBOSE *calling after him, bulls his way off.*)

MRS DUBOSE: If you aren't sent to the reform school before next week, my name's not Dubose!

(MRS DUBOSE *goes back into the house.*)

JEAN: Mrs Henry Lafayette Dubose. If she was on the porch when Jem or I passed, we'd be raked by her wrathful gaze, subjected to ruthless interrogation regarding our behaviour, and given a melancholy prediction on what we'd amount to when we grew up, which was always nothing. Jem and I hated her. We had no idea that she was fighting a hard battle.

(REVEREND SYKES, *a Negro minister, dressed conservatively in a black suit, black tie and white shirt, has come on stage.*)

REVEREND SYKES (*calling*): Miss Cal –

(CALPURNIA *is coming out onto the porch, followed by* SCOUT.)

JEAN: Reverend Sykes of the First Purchase Church – called First Purchase because it was paid for from the first earnings of the freed slaves.

CALPURNIA: Afternoon, Reverend.

REVEREND SYKES (*speaking quietly*): It's about Brother Tom Robinson's trouble. We have to do more for his wife and children.

CALPURNIA (*agreeing*): Yes, Reverend.

REVEREND SYKES: The collection for the next three Sundays will go to Helen. Please encourage everyone to bring what they can.

SCOUT (*curiously*): Why are you all taking up a collection for Tom Robinson's wife?

REVEREND SYKES: To tell you the truth, Miss Jean Louise, Helen's finding it hard to get work these days.

SCOUT: I know Tom Robinson's done somethin' awful, but why won't folks hire Helen?

Act I

REVEREND SYKES: Folks aren't anxious to –

(REVEREND SYKES *hesitates as he sees someone entering.*)

REVEREND SYKES (*dropping his voice*): – to have anything to do with his family.

(MAYELLA EWELL, *a poor girl accustomed to strenuous labour, has entered followed by her father,* BOB EWELL, *a little 'bantam cock' of a man, ignorant and sharp-tempered.*)

MAYELLA (*as they cross the stage*): Yes, Pa.
BOB EWELL: I told ya – stay outa town right now, hear?
MAYELLA (*resigned*): I hear.

(*They continue off.*)

JEAN (*quietly*): Bob Ewell – his daughter, Mayella. No truant officer could keep any of the Ewells in school. No public health officer could free them from filth and disease. Good times or bad, they lived off the county – in a cabin by the garbage dump near a small Negro settlement. (*She smiles wryly.*) And all Bob Ewell could hold onto that made him feel better than his nearest neighbours was that if scrubbed with lye soap in very hot water – his skin was white.
SCOUT (*puzzled*): Why'd you stop talking? Those are just Ewells.
JEAN: Remembering it now, I'm not surprised they stopped talking.
REVEREND SYKES: I have a lot of calls to make. Good-bye, Miss Jean Louise. See you Sunday, Miss Cal.
CALPURNIA (*nodding*): Reverend.
SCOUT (*after him*): 'Bye.

(REVEREND SYKES *exits.*)

SCOUT (*curious*): Cal – what did Tom Robinson do?

CALPURNIA: You mean, what do they *say* he did? Old Mr Bob Ewell accused Tom of attackin' his girl and had him put in jail.

SCOUT (*scornfully*): But everyone in Maycomb knows the Ewells. You'd think folks would be glad to hire Tom's wife.

CALPURNIA (*briefly*): That's what you think.

SCOUT (*not satisfied*): What does it mean – he attacked her?

CALPURNIA: You'll have to ask Mr Finch about that. You hungry?

SCOUT (*lighting up as she sees someone coming*): I have to see Atticus. There's Dill!

(CALPURNIA *re-enters house.*)

JEAN: That was the summer Dill came to us – Dill, who was to give us the idea of making Boo Radley come out.

(DILL *is coming on stage. He is a little older than* SCOUT, *small, blond and wise. He is neat, well-dressed with an undercurrent of sophistication, but his laugh is sudden and happy.*)

DILL (*looking up at* SCOUT): Hey.
SCOUT: Hey, Dill.

(*She comes down from the porch and crosses toward him.*)

JEAN: His real name was Charles Baker Harris, and he'd be sent here to spend the summer with an aunt. We came to know Dill as a pocket Merlin whose head teemed with eccentric plans, strange longings and quaint fancies. He was to be my childhood fiancé – which was nice for a girl, even if he wasn't very big. 'I'm little,' he said one time, 'but I'm old.'

DILL: You watchin' for your father?

SCOUT: That's right. (*Struck with sudden curiosity*) What about *your* daddy?

DILL (*cautiously*): What do you mean?

10

Act I

(JEM, *still carrying the football, is coming back on stage.*)

SCOUT: You never say anything about him.
DILL: Because I haven't got one.
SCOUT: Is he dead?
DILL: No.
SCOUT: Then if he isn't dead, you've got one, haven't you?

(DILL *is embarrassed.*)

JEM: Never mind her, Dill.
SCOUT (*exasperated*): If his father isn't dead, how can he say he hasn't got one?
JEM (*has taken her arm*): Scout!

(SCOUT *stops at his tone and turns to look with him at the door to the Radley place, which is opening.* NATHAN RADLEY, *a pale, thin, leathery man is coming out.*)

SCOUT (*relaxing; softly*): *Nathan* Radley.
JEAN: When old Mr Radley died some folks thought Boo might come out, but they had another think coming. Boo's older brother, Nathan – that's him – moved in and took his father's place. At least Nathan Radley would speak to us.

(NATHAN, *preoccupied, is passing by.*)

JEM (*nervously clearing his throat*): Hidy do, Mr Nathan.
NATHAN (*walking off*): Afternoon.
JEAN (*thoughtfully*): Looking back for a place to begin – perhaps it would be what happens next.

(*She considers this a moment, nods confirmation to herself and steps offstage. Meanwhile* SCOUT, JEM *and* DILL *have all turned to look back at the Radley place.*)

11

JEM: Now Boo Radley's in there all by himself.

DILL: Wonder what he does. Looks like he'd stick his head out the door some time.

JEM: He goes out when it's pitch dark. I've seen his tracks in our backyard many a morning, and one night I heard him scratching on the back screen.

DILL: Wonder what he looks like.

JEM (*professionally*): Judging from his tracks, he's about six and a half feet tall, he eats raw squirrels and any cats he can catch. What teeth he has are yellow and rotten. His eyes pop and most of the time he drools.

DILL (*with decision*): Let's make him come out.

SCOUT (*shocked*): Make Boo Radley come out?

JEM: If you want to get yourself killed, all you have to do is go up and knock on that door.

DILL (*challenging*): You're scared – too scared to put your big toe in the front yard.

JEM: Ain't scared, just respectful.

DILL: I dare you.

JEM (*trapped*): You dare me?

(JEM *turns to look at the house apprehensively.*)

SCOUT: Don't go near it, Jem.

DILL: You gonna run out on a dare?

JEM: Lemme think a minute.

DILL: Just *touch* the house. I dare you!

JEM: Touch the house, that's all?

DILL: He'll probably come out after you. Then Scout 'n me'll jump on him and hold him down till we can tell him, we just want to look at him.

(JEM *does not respond.*)

DILL (*impatiently*): Well?

JEM: Don't hurry me.

12

Act I

(JEM *starts slowly toward the house.*)

DILL: Scout and me's right behind you.

(*As* JEM *continues toward the Radley house, they follow,* SCOUT *pausing beside the tree.* JEM *hesitates.*)

DILL: Folks where I come from aren't so scared. I've never seen such scary folks as here.

(*That does it.* JEM *speeds to the house, slaps it with his palm, and races back past* SCOUT *and* DILL. DILL *follows.* SCOUT *starts to follow, notices something in a knothole in the tree, takes it, and then follows.*)

JEM (*panting with excitement*): So there –

(*They all turn and look back at the house.*)

DILL (*in a hushed voice*): Someone at the window! Look at the curtains!

(*The curtains have been pulled slightly to the side, and now they fall back into place.*)

JEM (*horrified*): He was watching! He saw me!
SCOUT (*exhausted*): Don't *ever* do that again. (*Absently putting a piece of chewing gum in her mouth*) If you get killed – what with Atticus already so old – what would become of me?
JEM (*considering her*): Where'd you get the chewing gum?
SCOUT (*as she chews, she nods toward the tree*): It was sticking in the knothole.
JEM (*shocked*): That tree? Spit it out! Right now!
SCOUT (*obeying, but indignant*): I was just getting the flavour.
JEM (*grimly*): Suppose Boo Radley put it there? Suppose it's poison? You go gargle!

SCOUT (*shaking her head*): It'd take the taste outa my mouth.

DILL (*still concentrating on the Radley house*): Let's throw a pebble against the door – and as soon as he sticks his head out, say we want to buy him an ice cream. (*Logically*) That'll seem friendly. Maybe if he came out, and sat a spell with us, he'd feel better.

SCOUT: How do you know he don't feel good now?

DILL (*concerned*): How'd you feel if you'd been shut up for a hundred years with nothing but cats to eat? (*Searching about*) 'Course, if you'd rather *I* throw the pebble –

JEM (*disgusted*): Better leave it to me. (*Apparently picking up a pebble*) How many times do I have to show you that –

DILL (*unimpressed*): Maybe you ran up and touched it, but –

SCOUT (*worried*): You're not going to throw a stone at the Radley house!

JEM (*to DILL, as he winds up to throw*): I guess I just have to keep on showing you –

(*He is stopped by an authoritative voice from offstage.*)

ATTICUS: Jem!

(*JEM stops and they all look toward the direction of the voice offstage.*)

DILL: Your father!

SCOUT (*at the same time*): Atticus!

(*ATTICUS, carrying an old briefcase and wearing his 'office' clothes, comes on. He is tall, quietly impressive, reserved, 'civilised' and nearly fifty. He wears glasses, and because of poor sight in his left eye, looks with his right eye when he wants to see something well.*)

ATTICUS (*trying to take in the situation; curiously*): Just what were you about to do, Jem?

14

JEM: Nothin' sir.

ATTICUS (*unwilling to be put off*): I don't want any of that. Tell me.

JEM: We were – (*Assuming responsibility*) I was going to throw a pebble – to get Boo Radley to come out.

ATTICUS: Why?

DILL: Because – sir.

(*As* ATTICUS *turns to him,* DILL *finishes lamely.*)

DILL: We thought he might enjoy us . . .

ATTICUS (*gravely*): I see. (*Turning back to* JEM, *with decision.*) Son, I'm going to tell you something and tell you one time. Don't bother that man.

SCOUT: But why doesn't he ever –

ATTICUS (*cutting in*): What Mr Radley does is his own business. If he wants to stay inside his own house, he has the right to stay inside – free from the attention of inquisitive children. How would you like it if I barged into your rooms at night without knocking?

JEM: That's different.

ATTICUS: Is it?

JEM: Because we're not crazy.

ATTICUS: What Mr Radley does might seem peculiar to us, but it does *not* seem peculiar to him.

JEM (*protesting*): Anyone who stays inside all the time and never –

ATTICUS (*cutting in*): But that's *his* decision. (*Considering them*) There's something I'd like to ask. If you'll do it, you'll get along a lot better with *all* kinds. You see, you never really understand a person until you consider things from his point of view.

JEM: Sir?

ATTICUS: Until you climb into his skin and walk around in it.

JEM (*incredulous*): You want us to consider things from Boo Radley's point of view?

DILL (*impatiently*): He means – everyone.

SCOUT: You stay outa this.

ATTICUS (*smiling*): Dill's right. But I expect I'm asking too much. There's Walter Cunningham.

(*With* ATTICUS *diverted*, DILL *speaks confidentially to* JEM *and* SCOUT, *with a nod toward the Radley house.*)

DILL: I've got a much better plan. (*Starting to go*) See you.

(MR CUNNINGHAM, *a farmer, carrying a sack, is coming on, as* DILL *runs off past him.*)

ATTICUS (*calling*): Afternoon, Walter. (*Aside to* JEM *and* SCOUT, *using Dill's confidential tone and nod*) Regardless of any plans, you're to stay away from that house unless invited.

MR CUNNINGHAM (*holding out the sack*): This is for you, Mr Finch. Turnip greens.

ATTICUS (*accepting the sack gravely*): Thank you very much.

MR CUNNINGHAM: I'd like to pay cash for your services, but between the mortgage and the entailment –

ATTICUS: This is just fine. Jem, please take this sack to Cal.

(JEM *takes the sack and goes inside.*)

ATTICUS: I'd say your bill is settled, Walter.

MR CUNNINGHAM (*doubtfully*): You put in a lot of time.

ATTICUS: Let's see now. You left a load of stove wood in the backyard, then a sack of hickory nuts. At Christmas there was a crate of smilax and holly. Now a bag of turnip greens. I'm more than paid.

MR CUNNINGHAM: If you say so.

SCOUT: Your boy's in my class at school, Mr Cunningham. (*Uneasily, as she recalls*) We had a disagreement the other day.

MR CUNNINGHAM (*smiling*): I have a few with that boy myself, little lady.

SCOUT (*concerned*): I didn't actually beat him up bad.

MR CUNNINGHAM (*amused*): If he can't defend himself against a girl, he'll just have to take it. (*To* ATTICUS, *as he goes*) Much obliged, Mr Finch.

ATTICUS (*after him*): Any time I can be of help.

SCOUT (*curious*): Why does he pay with stove wood and turnip greens?

ATTICUS: Because that's the only way he can.

SCOUT: Are *we* poor, Atticus?

ATTICUS: We are indeed.

SCOUT: As poor as the Cunninghams?

ATTICUS: Not exactly. The Cunninghams are country folks and the depression hits them hardest. (*Curious*) What was your trouble with my client's boy?

SCOUT: He said some things I didn't like. (*Shrugs*) I rubbed his nose in the dirt.

ATTICUS: That's not very ladylike. What'd he say?

(JEM *is coming back onto the porch with his football.*)

SCOUT: Things. And I think we should have a talk. I've been watching for you to get home because –

(*She is interrupted by* JEM, *who is cocking his arm to pass the football.*)

JEM: Atticus! Catch!

ATTICUS (*making no move*): Hang onto it, son. Not today.

JEM (*coming down off the porch*): Atticus, will you be going out for the Methodists? For the football game?

ATTICUS: What game?

JEM (*eagerly*): It won't be till fall, but everyone's talking about it already. It's for fundraising. The Methodists challenged the Baptists to a game of touch football.

ATTICUS (*smiling*): 'Afraid I wouldn't be of much help, Jem.

JEM: Everybody in town's father is playing.

— ATTICUS (*going up onto the porch*): Except yours.

JEM (*insisting*): Every other father –

ATTICUS (*cheerfully*): I'd break my neck.

JEM: It's *touch*.

ATTICUS: I'm too old for that sort of thing.

JEM (*unhappily; taking a breath*): Sir – would you have time to show Scout 'n me how to shoot our air rifles? Later, I mean?

ATTICUS (*sorry to be a disappointment*): I've told you – you'll have to wait for your Uncle Jack. (*Encouragingly*) He'll *really* show you.

(ATTICUS *seems to be missing the point.*)

JEM: Couldn't *you* show us?

ATTICUS (*as a simple statement of fact*): I'm not interested in guns.

(ATTICUS *goes into the house.* JEM, *disappointed and disturbed, turns back to* SCOUT.)

JEM: He's not interested in *anything*!

(*With all his strength,* JEM *throws the football offstage.*)

SCOUT (*unimpressed*): Now you'll have to chase after it. (*Nodding to one side; curious*) Jem – why do folks slow down as they go past?

JEM (*turning*): What folks?

(*He follows the direction of Scout's gaze. Voices are heard from that direction offstage.*)

VOICE (*unfriendly*): Yonder's some Finches.

ANOTHER VOICE: Them's his chill'un!

ANOTHER VOICE: For all *he* cares, blacks c'n run loose and rip up the countryside.

SCOUT (*perplexed*): Why is everybody –
JEM (*dismissing them*): Because that's the way they are.
SCOUT: But why –
JEM (*not wanting to continue; going*): I have to get my football.

(*As* JEM *runs off,* ATTICUS *comes back onto the porch.*)

ATTICUS: Someone call?
SCOUT: I've been meaning to ask – (*She takes a breath*) Atticus, do you defend niggers?
ATTICUS (*startled*): Of course I do. Don't say 'nigger,' Scout. That's common.
SCOUT: 'S what everybody at school says.
ATTICUS: From now on it'll be everybody less one.
SCOUT: Do all lawyers defend N–Negroes?
ATTICUS: They do.
SCOUT (*exasperated*): Then why do the kids at school make it sound like you're doin' somethin' awful?
ATTICUS: You aren't old enough to understand some things yet, Scout, but there's been a lot of high talk around town that I shouldn't do much about defending Tom Robinson. (*Firmly*) But I'm going to defend that man.
SCOUT: If they say you shouldn't, why are you doing it?
ATTICUS (*considering this*): The main reason: if I didn't defend him, I couldn't hold my head up.

(ATTICUS *looks at* SCOUT *and smiles.*)

ATTICUS: I couldn't even tell you or Jem not to do something again.
SCOUT: You mean Jem and me wouldn't have to mind you any more?
ATTICUS: That's about right.
SCOUT: Why?
ATTICUS: Because I could never *ask* you to mind me again. Every lawyer gets at least one case in his lifetime that affects him personally. This one's mine, I guess.

SCOUT: Are we going to win it?

ATTICUS: No, honey.

SCOUT: Then, why –

ATTICUS: Simply because we were licked a hundred years before we started is no reason for us not to *try* to win.

SCOUT: You sound like some old Confederate veteran.

ATTICUS: Only we aren't fighting Yankees. We'll be fighting our friends. But remember this, no matter how bitter things get, they're still our friends and this is still our home.

SCOUT (*confused*): Is there something you want me to do, Atticus?

ATTICUS (*nodding*): Keep your head – even if things turn ugly. And I hope you can get through what's coming without catching Maycomb's usual disease. Why reasonable people go stark raving mad when anything involving a Negro comes up is something I don't pretend to understand.

SCOUT: The Tom Robinson case must be pretty important.

ATTICUS (*speaking quietly*): It goes to the essence of a man's conscience.

SCOUT (*concerned for him*): Suppose you're wrong about it?

ATTICUS: How's that?

SCOUT: Most people think they're right and you're wrong.

ATTICUS: They're entitled to think that, and they're entitled to full respect for their opinions. (*Ready to go back into the house*) But before I can live with other folks, I've got to live with myself.

SCOUT: What does that mean?

ATTICUS (*pauses; smiling*): One thing *doesn't* abide by majority rule – a person's conscience.

(ATTICUS *goes on into the house.* SCOUT *looks after him a moment, then turns and looks offstage.*)

SCOUT (*calling*): Jem – (*Eager to talk to him; she hurries offstage*) Jem – Hey!

(*As* SCOUT *goes off,* JEAN *steps back on stage.*)

JEAN: I thought I had interesting information to pass along to Jem. Apparently, our father was more complex than we'd realised. Certainly this new aspect of his legal practice was more promising than doing papers in an office. (*Shaking her head as she recalls*) I found my brother unresponsive. Probably the Tom Robinson case wasn't quite as new to him as it was to me. Thinking about it now, probably it was abuse from older boys that made Jem so eager to involve his father in sensible community activities – like a game of touch football. All such invitations were politely declined. Then a few weeks later something happened – something that made our father even more of a puzzle. The tension in the town about the approaching trial was getting drum-tight, but what happened had nothing to do with that – it had to do with a liver-coloured bird dog named Tim.

(JEM *and* SCOUT *are coming back on, with* JEM *pulling* SCOUT *along.*)

SCOUT (*protesting*): *Why* do I have to come home?
JEM: Because I tell you. (*Concerned*) That old dog from down yonder is sick. (*Calling*) Cal, can you come out a minute.
SCOUT: It's only Tim, and he's gone lopsided, that's all.

(CALPURNIA *comes out onto the porch, wiping her hands on a tea towel.*)

CALPURNIA: What is it, Jem? I can't come out every time you want me.
JEM: Somethin' wrong with that old dog down yonder.
CALPURNIA (*sighing*): I can't wrap up any dog's foot right now.
JEM: He's sick, Cal. Somethin' wrong with him.
CALPURNIA (*finally interested*): Tryin' to catch his tail?
JEM: No, he's doin' like this.

(JEM *gulps, like a goldfish, hunching his shoulders and twisting his torso, while* CALPURNIA *watches narrowly.*)

CALPURNIA (*her voice hardening*): You tellin' me a story, Jem Finch?

JEM: No, Cal. And he's coming this way.

CALPURNIA: Runnin'?

JEM (*shaking his head*): Just moseyin' – but walkin' funny.

CALPURNIA (*that decides her*): I'll call help.

(*She pauses before hurrying into house.*)

CALPURNIA: You two get in off the street.

(CALPURNIA *hurries inside.*)

JEM (*to* SCOUT): Come on.

SCOUT (*reluctantly coming up onto the porch with* JEM): He's not even in sight.

CALPURNIA (*voice offstage, loud and anxious; apparently on the telephone*): Operator, hello – Miss Eula May, ma-am? Please gimme Mr Finch's office – right away!

SCOUT (*to* JEM): You started something.

CALPURNIA (*offstage, half-shouting*): Mr Finch, this is Cal. There's a mad dog down the street a piece. Jem says he's comin' this way! Yes – yessir – yes!

(*She hangs up.*)

JEM (*calling in*): What's Atticus say?

CALPURNIA (*offstage, calling back*): In a minute.

(*She rattles the telephone hook and then speaks loudly again.*)

CALPURNIA: Miss Eula May. I'm through talking to Mr Finch. Listen, can you call Miss Crawford, Miss Atkinson and whoever's got a phone on this street and tell 'em a mad dog's comin'? Please, ma-am ... hurry!

SCOUT: What about the Radleys? They got a phone?

Act I

(CALPURNIA *is coming back onto the porch.*)

JEM: They wouldn't come out anyway.
SCOUT: Maybe Nathan –

(*She comes down off the porch and goes toward the Radley house.*)

SCOUT: I better call out to them.

(*Both* CALPURNIA *and* JEM *go after her.*)

JEM: No, Scout.
CALPURNIA (*catching her*): Listen to me – go back and you stay.
SCOUT: I just want to shout to the Radleys.
CALPURNIA: You go back!

(CALPURNIA *races up onto the Radley porch where she starts banging on the door, at the same time casting about nervous glances.*)

SCOUT (*softly; impressed*): She's not scared one bit.
JEM (*cautiously moving*): I don't see Tim.
SCOUT (*following* JEM): Maybe he turned off.
JEM: Maybe.
CALPURNIA (*meanwhile banging on the Radley door*): Mr Nathan –
Mr Boo! Mad dog's comin'! Mad dog's comin'! Hear me?
Don't come outside. Mad dog!

(*During this,* SCOUT *has noticed something in the tree knothole and she takes it.*)

JEM (*suddenly tense as he watches*): I see him! There he is! Cal!
(*Grabbing* SCOUT) Get back!

(CALPURNIA *runs down to join them. She herds them ahead of her with anxious glances back.*)

23

CALPURNIA: Both of you – inside the house and stay inside!

(CALPURNIA *pauses to look back.*)

CALPURNIA: That Tim's gone mad all right!

(SCOUT *has stopped to shout back at the silent Radley house.*)

SCOUT: He's comin' now, Mr Radley!

CALPURNIA (*giving* SCOUT *a fierce swat on the seat*): Git inside!

SCOUT (*muttering bitterly as she goes up onto the porch*): You always pick on me.

JEM: You had it coming.

SCOUT (*pointing and justifying herself*): He's moving slow as a snail.

(*They have all turned on the porch to watch Tim's 'approach' offstage.* SCOUT *starts inspecting a small box she is holding.*)

JEM: What's that?

SCOUT: Finders-keepers.

JEM (*watching for Tim again*): Where'd you find it?

SCOUT: Where I found the chewing gum – that old knothole.

(JEM *is startled into looking at* SCOUT *again.*)

JEM: The Radley tree?

(SCOUT *shrugs her indifference.*)

CALPURNIA (*watching intently; softly*): Please come soon, Mr Finch.

JEM: What's inside?

SCOUT (*inspecting*): Two pennies – all slicked up.

JEM (*impressed*): Indian-heads. They're real valuable. They make you have good luck. Why would someone leave valuable Indian-head pennies –

SCOUT (*protectively*): They're mine. (*Pointing*) I risked my life out there!

JEM (*considering the situation offstage again*): Old Tim's walkin' like his right legs are shorter than his left legs.

(*They all lean forward to watch. From offstage there is the sound of an automobile approaching.*)

JEAN: We assumed that Atticus would turn to competent authority to handle this dangerous situation, and our assumption was to prove correct.

(*The sound of the approaching car comes to a stop.*)

JEAN: When our father arrived, he was accompanied by the sheriff.

(ATTICUS *comes on with* HECK TATE, *who carries a heavy rifle. They go past* JEAN *as though she is not there and pause by the far edge of the porch.*)

JEM (*Going down to join them*): Atticus – he's over there behind...

ATTICUS: Stay on the porch, son.

CALPURNIA: Back behind the Radley pecan trees.

HECK: Not runnin', is he, Cal?

CALPURNIA: He's in the twitchin' stage, Mr Heck.

(HECK *watches carefully as he advances a few steps.*)

HECK: Usually they go in a straight line, but you never can tell.

ATTICUS (*following behind* HECK): The slope will probably bring him back onto the road.

SCOUT (*to* CALPURNIA): I thought mad dogs foamed at the mouth and jumped at your throat.

CALPURNIA: Hush.

ATTICUS (*softly*): There he is.

SCOUT: He just looks sick.

HECK (*aside to* ATTICUS). He's got it all right, Mr Finch.

JEM (*calling*): Is he looking for a place to die, Mr Heck?

HECK (*over his shoulder*): Far from dead, Jem. He hasn't got started yet.

ATTICUS: He's within range, Heck. You better get him before he goes down a side street. Lord knows who's around the corner. (*Calling back*) Cal –

CALPURNIA (*understanding; to* JEM *and* SCOUT): Inside the house – both of you.

JEM (*temporising*): If he gets closer . . .

SCOUT (*clutching the porch rail tightly with both hands*): I don't go in till he goes in.

JEM: I wanta watch the sheriff!

JEAN: It was right then – the most astonishing thing happened. Jem and I almost fainted!

(HECK *turns and offers the rifle to* ATTICUS.)

HECK: You take him, Mr Finch. You do it.

JEAN: We thought the sheriff must've lost his mind.

ATTICUS (*urgently*): Don't waste time, Heck! Go on!

HECK: Mr Finch – this is a one-shot job.

ATTICUS (*vehemently*): Don't just stand there, Heck!

HECK (*frantic*): Look where he is! For God's sake, Mr Finch! I can't shoot that well and you know it.

ATTICUS: I haven't shot a gun in thirty years.

(HECK *shoves the rifle into Atticus' hands.*)

HECK: I'd feel mighty comfortable if you did now.

(*Holding the rifle,* ATTICUS *decides to accept the responsibility and, watching carefully, he moves forward several steps.*)

JEAN (*as this is happening*): Jem and I were in a fog – watching our father standing there in the street with a rifle. Others were watching, too, but we didn't know it then. It didn't make any sense at all. It was utterly beyond belief.

(ATTICUS *has taken off his glasses, and still keeping watch, he drops them on the street. He rubs one eye and blinks. Then his body goes tense as he focuses totally on the mad dog offstage.*)

CALPURNIA (*her hands to her cheeks*): Sweet Jesus, help him.

(ATTICUS *works the bolt action, apparently slamming a cartridge into the chamber, raises the rifle quickly, and fires.*)

HECK (*a shout*): Got him! (*Happy and relieved, as he hurries off*) You got him!

ATTICUS (*after him*): Yes, but I think I was a little to the right. (*Muttering as he picks up his glasses*) If I had my druthers, I'd take a shotgun!

(HECK *is re-entering.*)

HECK: Dead as a doornail. (*As though it's news.*) Just a *little* to the right.

ATTICUS (*handing the rifle back to* HECK): Always was.

(*Porch doors are opening, and* MISS STEPHANIE *and* MISS MAUDIE *are cautiously coming out.*)

HECK: I'll have someone come down with a pick-up and take him away.

(ATTICUS *stops* JEM *and* SCOUT, *who are coming down off the porch.*)

ATTICUS: You stay where you are.

HECK: You haven't forgot much, Mr Finch. They say it never leaves you.

JEM (*calling*): Atticus –
ATTICUS: Yes, Jem?
JEM: I – I didn't know –
MISS MAUDIE (*from her porch*): I saw that, One-Shot Finch.

(ATTICUS *shakes his head at her and turns back to his son.*)

ATTICUS: Jem – you and your sister stay away from that dog. He's just as dangerous dead as alive.
JEM: Yes, sir. Atticus?
ATTICUS: What, son?
HECK (*amused at* JEM's *hesitation*): What's the matter, boy, can't you talk? Didn't you know your daddy's –
ATTICUS: Hush, Heck. Let's get back to town.
HECK: What's your hurry now? (*Good-humoured teasing*) Have to get back to workin' up your speeches for the trial?
ATTICUS (*as they go; wryly*): Don't remind me.

(*They go offstage.* CALPURNIA *goes inside the house.*)

MISS STEPHANIE: Maybe Tim wasn't really mad. Maybe he was just full of fleas – and Atticus Finch shot him dead.
MISS MAUDIE: If that Tim was still comin' up the street, maybe you'd be singing a different tune.
MISS STEPHANIE (*agreeing*): Maybe I would. (*As she is going back into the house*) I'll admit I felt safer when I saw Atticus take the rifle.
JEM (*still in shock*): Did you see him, Scout? All of a sudden it looked like that gun was a part of him. He did it so quick – I hafta aim for ten minutes 'fore I can hit somethin'.
MISS MAUDIE (*with a wicked smile*): Well, now, Miss Jean Louise. Still think your father can't do anything? Still ashamed of him?
SCOUT (*meekly*): No, ma'am.
MISS MAUDIE: Forgot to mention the other day that he was the deadest shot in Maycomb County.
JEM: Dead shot –

MISS MAUDIE: Something for you to think about, Jem Finch. When he was a boy his nickname was Ol' One-Shot. Why, if he shot fifteen times and hit fourteen doves, he'd complain about wasting ammunition.

JEM: But he never said anything about it.

SCOUT: Wonder why he never goes huntin' now.

MISS MAUDIE: If your father's anything, he's civilised. Marksmanship like that's a gift of God. I think maybe he put his gun down when he realised God had given him an unfair advantage.

SCOUT: Looks like he'd be proud of it.

MISS MAUDIE (*going*): People like your father never bother about pride in their gifts.

(MISS MAUDIE *re-enters her house.*)

JEAN: This bewildering event unsettled our established view of Atticus. It was something to talk over – no, celebrate! (*Wryly*) But we didn't get far.

(MRS DUBOSE *is coming out onto her porch.*)

SCOUT (*filled with anticipation*): Will I have something to tell 'em at school on Monday!

JEM: Don't know if we should say anything about it.

SCOUT (*coming down off the porch*): I'd like to find the Cunningham boy right now! Ain't everybody's daddy the deadest shot in Maycomb County.

JEM (*following her*): I reckon if he'd wanted us to know, he'da told us.

SCOUT: Maybe it just slipped his mind.

JEM: Naw, it's something you wouldn't understand. (*Blazing with this new pride*) We don't have to talk about it any more'n he does – but we know! (*To the sky*) An' I don't care if he's a hundred years old!

SCOUT (*calling out*): Hey, Mrs Dubose! Did you see my father –

MRS DUBOSE: Don't say 'hey' to me, you ugly girl! You say 'Good afternoon, Mrs Dubose.'

JEAN: In point of fact Jem and I didn't get to the end of the street before we'd been slapped down again about our father.

MRS DUBOSE: You should be in a dress and camisole, young lady. If somebody doesn't change your ways, you'll grow up waiting on tables. A Finch waiting on tables at the O.K. Cafe – hah!

(SCOUT, *upset, reaches out and takes* JEM's *hand.*)

JEAN: I was terrified. The O.K. Cafe was a dim organisation at the edge of town. (*As she recalls*) We still didn't know what was really the matter with Mrs Dubose – but that's part of what Atticus wanted us to do – part of why I'm trying to remember it all now.

(JEAN *steps offstage. Meanwhile* JEM *has disentangled his hand from that of his uneasy sister.*)

JEM (*aside to her; whispering*): Come on, Scout. Don't pay any attention. Just hold your head high – and be a gentleman.

(SCOUT *decides to make the effort, and they start walking again. However,* MRS DUBOSE *will not let them alone.*)

MRS DUBOSE: A lovelier lady than your mother never lived. It's shocking the way Atticus Finch lets her children run wild.

(JEM *hesitates.*)

SCOUT (*whispering*): I'm with you.

JEM (*whispering back*): We'll keep walking.

MRS DUBOSE: Not only a Finch waiting on tables, but one in the courthouse, lawing for niggers!

(JEM, *stung hard, stops short.*)

SCOUT (*whispering, anxiously*): Let's keep goin', Jem.
MRS DUBOSE (*as she's going back inside*): What's this world come
   to with the Finches going against their raising? (*Her parting
   shot*) Your father's no better than the trash he works for!

(*With this, she completes her exit, leaving* SCOUT *hurt and* JEM
stunned.)

JEM (*gasping*): I'll – I'll fix her!
SCOUT: Hold your head high, Jem, an' –
JEM: She has no right –
SCOUT (*trying to hold him*): Jem –
JEM (*shoving her hands away*): Just because Atticus – I'm sick
   and tired – everybody –

(JEM *races up onto Mrs Dubose's porch, where he starts tearing up
the potted flowers there.*)

SCOUT (*frantic*): Jem! Come back!
JEM (*shouting back*): Go home! Stay outa this!

(*As the shocked* SCOUT *feels her way back toward her porch,* JEM
*turns, having completed the destruction of Mrs Dubose's porch
flowers, and rushes off, apparently intent on further objects for his
fury.*)

SCOUT (*after him; a cry*): Jem!

(*But* JEM, *past hearing, has gone. Frightened,* SCOUT *goes back
onto her porch, from where she watches anxiously.* DILL *dressed in
different clothes – dusty and untidy – comes on.*)

DILL (*subdued*): Hey, Scout.

SCOUT (DILL's *presence only half-registering*): Jem's outa control!
He's gone mad! (*Looking back*) He's knocking the tops off
every camellia bush Mrs Dubose owns!

DILL (*impressed*): Thought Jem had a slow fuse.

SCOUT: Not any more. He's gone crazy.

DILL: From people sayin' things about your father?

SCOUT: Yes – Mrs Dubose – (*Stops herself; curiously*) How'd you
know?

(DILL *shrugs.*)

SCOUT (*Eager for* DILL *to know*): We found out somethin' about
Atticus today – somethin' special.

DILL (*not surprised*): About time.

SCOUT (*bursting with it*): He's the deadest shot in Maycomb!

(*This is not what* DILL *expects.*)

DILL (*disappointed*): That's what you found out?

SCOUT (*nodding*): It's the truth. So it doesn't matter *what* folks
say.

DILL: Wouldn't matter anyway.

(SCOUT *becomes aware that they are not quite talking about the
same thing. She considers him.*)

SCOUT: What are you doing here? I thought you'd been taken
back to stay with your folks in Meridian?

DILL (*uneasily*): I – I was.

SCOUT: Then how in the Sam Hill –

DILL: It's – you see –

SCOUT (*as his appearance finally registers*): You're all mussed 'n'
dusty.

DILL: 'Course I am. (*he takes a quick breath*) I have a new father,
and he doesn't like me – so he had me bound in chains and
left to die in the basement. But I was secretly kept alive on

raw field beans by a passing farmer who heard my cries for help.

SCOUT: If you were chained up in the basement –

DILL: The good man poked a bushel of beans to me – pod by pod – through the ventilator!

(*During this,* JEM *is coming back on stage at the point where he went off. Aghast at himself, he is moving slowly toward the porch, not yet noticed by the others.*)

SCOUT (*hooked*): Lucky for you that good man was passing.

DILL (*sure of himself now*): I worked myself free – pulling the chains from the walls. Then – still in wrist irons – I wandered out of Meridian where I discovered a small animal show – and they hired me to wash the camel.

SCOUT: How do you go about washing a –

DILL (*pressing on*): I travelled all over with that show – everywhere – till suddenly my sense of direction told me I was just across the river from Maycomb. (*He gulps a quick breath*) What I did then –

(JEM *has come up on the last of this, still unnoticed.*)

JEM (*cutting in*): How *did* you get here, Dill?

DILL: Hey, Jem.

SCOUT: Jem – (*Suddenly it comes back; horrified*) Jem – what did you –

JEM (*cutting her off*): I was speaking to Dill.

DILL (*sighing; undramatic*): I took thirteen dollars from my mother's purse, caught the nine o'clock train from Meridian, got off at the junction, and walked the rest of the way.

JEM: Why'd you run off?

DILL: Didn't run off. Decided I'd come back here, that's all.

SCOUT: You want to stay with your Aunt Rachel?

DILL: I want to stay here.

SCOUT: With us?

JEM (*grim*): We're gonna have a hot summer.

DILL: I don't care.

(ATTICUS *is hurrying on stage.*)

SCOUT (*warningly*): Jem –

(ATTICUS *walks past them over to the front of the Dubose house, and for a moment he considers it.*)

JEM (*aside to* DILL; *nervously*): Maybe you better come back later.

DILL (*hushed*): I'm not going.

(ATTICUS *turns and walks back toward the group.*)

SCOUT (*bravely*): Look at this, Atticus – we've got a visitor. Here's Dill – come back from Meridian. (*Trying to fill the awkward silence*) He knows how to wash a camel.

ATTICUS (*gravely acknowledging him*): Dill.

DILL (*swallowing*): Sir.

ATTICUS (*a suggestion of winter in his voice*): Jem – I had a phone call a few minutes ago. Are you responsible for the damage to those flowers?

JEM: Yes, sir.

ATTICUS: Why'd you do it?

JEM (*softly*): Mrs Dubose said you lawed for niggers.

ATTICUS (*getting it straight*): And that's why you destroyed her garden?

JEM (*swallowing*): Yes, sir.

ATTICUS: Son, I have no doubt you've been annoyed by your contemporaries about me lawing for niggers, as you say, but to do something like this to a sick old lady is inexcusable. I strongly advise you to go over and have a talk with Mrs Dubose.

JEM (*startled*): Talk to her!

ATTICUS: Right now.

34

JEM: But –
ATTICUS: Go on, Jem.
SCOUT: But – sir –
ATTICUS (*stopping her*): Scout.
JEM (*getting himself together*): All right. I'll go talk to her.
ATTICUS (*unmoved*): Come straight home afterwards.

(JEM *goes toward the Dubose house like a man walking bravely to his execution. During the following speeches, he goes up to her door, knocks, and is let in.*)

SCOUT (*to* ATTICUS): All he was doin' was standin' up for you!
ATTICUS (*as he looks after* JEM): Never thought Jem'd be the one to lose his head. (*Turning toward* SCOUT) Thought I'd have more trouble with you.
SCOUT: Why do we have to keep our heads anyway? Nobody at school has to keep his head about anything.
ATTICUS (*not happy about it*): You'll soon have to be keeping your head about far worse things. (*Turning to* DILL) Your Aunt Rachel didn't mention you were coming back.
SCOUT: She doesn't know.
DILL: Please, Mr Finch – don't tell her I'm here.
ATTICUS: Don't tell her –
SCOUT: He's run away.
DILL: *Don't* make me go back, sir!
ATTICUS: Just let me get this straight –
DILL: If you make me go back, I'll run away again.
ATTICUS: Whoa, son.
SCOUT: He's been living on raw beans.
DILL (*nervously*): Scout –
ATTICUS: Let me do a little telephoning. (*Not letting* DILL *interrupt*) I'll ask if you could spend the night – perhaps stay a few days.
DILL (*hopefully*): Would you, sir?
ATTICUS (*as he goes inside*): Maybe Scout can get you something to go with the raw beans.

DILL (*after him*): Oh, I'm fine. Not hungry at all.

(ATTICUS *smiles as he enters the house.*)

SCOUT (*regarding* DILL *critically*): I'd think you'd be starving.

(DILL *shrugs.*)

SCOUT (*her suspicions growing*): Was your father really hateful like you said?

DILL (*unhappy*): That wasn't it, he – they just wasn't interested in me.

SCOUT: You're not telling me right. Your folks couldn't do without you.

DILL: Yes, they can. They get on a lot better without me. They stay gone most of the time, and when they're home, they're always off by themselves. And – I can't help them any. (*Being fair*) They're not mean. They buy me everything I want, but then it's – (*Imitating a man's voice*) – now you've – got – it – go – play – with – it.

SCOUT: They must need you. Why, Atticus couldn't get along a day without my help and advice.

DILL (*struggling with an idea*): The special thing about your father – it isn't that he's a dead shot, it's –

SCOUT (*highly critical*): He made Jem go over to Mrs Dubose.

DILL: Don't you see why he did that?

SCOUT (*unimpressed*): Because it's his way.

DILL (*agreeing*): And Jem'll be all right. (*Trying to catch her interest*) If I get to stay a few days, I have a new plan for bringing out Boo Radley.

SCOUT (*turning to look at the Radley house*): Why do you reckon Boo Radley's never run off?

DILL: Maybe he doesn't have anywhere to run off to. (*Back to business*) For my plan, we'll need a box of lemon drops. I'll put one just outside his door – and then a row of them down the street.

Act I

(ATTICUS *is coming back onto the porch, but* DILL *is too wrapped up in his scheme to see him.*)

DILL: When he thinks he's safe, he'll come out to pick up the lemon drop.

(DILL's *pantomiming is leading him toward the still unseen* ATTICUS.)

DILL: Then he'll notice the next one – then on to the next – he'll follow like an ant – then another – then –

(*The place for the next imaginary sweet is occupied by Atticus' shoes.* DILL *stops and looks up.*)

ATTICUS (*smiling*): That's a lot of lemon drops.

DILL (*uneasily*): We were foolin', sir.

ATTICUS: You've been the subject of considerable conversation.

DILL: What'd Aunt Rachel say?

ATTICUS: At first it came under the heading of: 'Wait till they get you home.' Then it was, 'His folks must be out of their minds worrying.' She went on to, 'That's all the Harris in him coming out,' and she ended with 'Reckon he can stay on for tonight anyway.'

DILL (*delighted*): Hey! (*To* SCOUT) Hear that!

ATTICUS: But I thought I'd better speak to your parents, so I called them, too.

DILL (*suddenly serious*): What'd they say?

ATTICUS: Couldn't've been more agreeable. (*Smiling*) They said you could stay on for as long as you're not in the way.

(SCOUT *gives a gasp of pleasure.*)

DILL (*subdued*): I see.

SCOUT: Great! Isn't that great?

DILL (*with an effort*): Sure is. (*To* ATTICUS, *trying to draw him out*) Guess they were looking all over Meridian for me.

ATTICUS (*shaking his head and smiling*): No, they thought you were probably stuck at some picture show.

DILL (*disappointed, but smiling back*): Generally, they'd be right, too.

ATTICUS (*becoming aware of* DILL'*s problem*): We'll be going through quite a difficult time, Dill. It'll be good having you with us.

DILL: Do you mean –

ATTICUS: It'll be a help having you here. There's a cot in Jem's room.

(HECK TATE *is coming on stage.*)

DILL: *Thank* you, sir. Thank you *very* much.

HECK (*calling*): Mr Finch.

ATTICUS: More company. Come on up, Heck.

HECK (*reserved*): Rather speak with you down here.

ATTICUS (*thoughtfully*): Oh?

SCOUT (*aside to her father*): What is it?

ATTICUS: Only two reasons why grown men talk in the front yard – death or politics. (*Calling*) Which is it, Heck?

HECK (*wryly*): Could be a little of both, Mr Finch.

ATTICUS (*considering this*): Then we'd better talk. (*He pauses. To* SCOUT) Maybe you and Dill can give Calpurnia a hand.

SCOUT: I want to know what's happening.

ATTICUS (*firmly*): You'll stay here. (*Glancing toward him*) Dill?

(DILL *takes hold of Scout's arm, as* ATTICUS *crosses over to* HECK.)

SCOUT (*jerking her arm free*): Don't get any idea you can boss me, too!

(SCOUT *crosses over to the porch swing.*)

DILL (*following; apologetically*): They have business.

(HECK *has turned aside and speaks confidentially to* ATTICUS.)

HECK: They moved Tom Robinson to the county jail this afternoon. I don't look for trouble, but I can't guarantee there won't be any.

ATTICUS: Don't be foolish, Heck. This is Maycomb.

HECK: I'm just uneasy, that's all.

ATTICUS: Trial'll probably begin day after tomorrow. You can keep him till then, can't you? (*Smiling*) I don't think anybody'll begrudge me a client with times this hard.

HECK (*smiling back*): It's just that Old Sarum bunch. You know how they do when they get shinnied up.

ATTICUS: Are they drinking?

HECK: Could be. (*Worried*) I don't see why you touched this case. You've got everything to lose.

ATTICUS (*quietly*): Do you really think so?

(*At this,* SCOUT *comes to the porch rail followed by* DILL.)

HECK (*taking breath; frankly*): Yes, I do, Atticus. I mean – everything.

ATTICUS (*with decision*): Heck, that boy might go to the chair, but he's not going till the truth's told.

HECK (*resigned*): Okay, Mr Finch.

ATTICUS: And you know as well as I do what the truth is.

(JEM, *coming from the Dubose house, pauses as he sees* HECK *and his father*.)

HECK (*withdrawn*): Just thought I should keep you informed.

ATTICUS: And I appreciate it, Heck. Thank you.

HECK (*relaxing again*): Sure – Well, take care of yourself.

(HECK *goes offstage.*)

ATTICUS (*after him; smiling*): Don't worry. (*As* JEM *approaches*) Well, son?

JEM: I told her I'd work on her garden and try to make it grow back. And I said I was sorry – but I'm not. What was Heck Tate –

ATTICUS (*cutting in*): No point in saying you're sorry, if you aren't.

JEM: How about what *she* said?

ATTICUS: She's old and she's ill. (*Going back into the house*) I have work.

JEM (*after him*): She wants me to read to her.

(ATTICUS *pauses.*)

JEM: She wants me to come over every afternoon and read out loud for two hours. Atticus – do I have to?

ATTICUS: You do.

JEM (*protesting*): Her house is so dark – creepy – shadows on the ceiling.

ATTICUS (*smiling grimly*): That should appeal to your imagination. (*As he goes*) Just pretend you're inside the Radley house.

(JEM *looks after* ATTICUS.)

JEM (*perplexed*): He's sure in a peculiar mood these days. (*Turning to* DILL *and* SCOUT) What'd Heck want?

DILL (*dramatic*): Death and politics!

SCOUT: Don't be silly. It was just they moved Tom Robinson to the Maycomb jail.

DILL (*to* JEM): Your father said I could stay. He said I could take the cot in your room.

SCOUT: What are you gonna read to Mrs Dubose?

JEM: *Ivanhoe*. (*Perplexed*) Why would she want me to read aloud?

DILL: Seemed like your father wasn't surprised.

40

Act I

(ATTICUS *is coming back onto the porch with* CALPURNIA. *He is carrying a small folding chair and an electrical extension cord with a light bulb at the end.*)

JEM (*anxiously, to* DILL): Why wouldn't he be surprised?

DILL: Ask him.

ATTICUS: Ask me what?

JEM: Nothin'.

ATTICUS: You folks'll be in bed when I come back, so I'll say good night now.

SCOUT: Where are you goin'?

ATTICUS: Out. You mind Calpurnia.

JEM: What are you doin' with the chair and light bulb?

ATTICUS: Might have use for them. (*As he goes*) Look after things, Cal.

CALPURNIA: Do my best, Mr Finch.

(ATTICUS *goes offstage.*)

SCOUT (*turning to* CALPURNIA): Where's he goin'?

CALPURNIA (*looking after* ATTICUS; *a little grimly*): I could make a guess – only I won't. Almost time for dinner. You get washed – all three of you.

(CALPURNIA *goes back inside.*)

DILL: I really need a wash.

SCOUT: That's the main thing Cal thinks about. Why wouldn't she make a guess?

(*No one has an answer to this.*)

JEM: Why was Atticus takin' a chair an' a light bulb?

(*No one has the answer to this either, and they start to go inside. As they are going* JEM *speaks.*)

JEM: What else was Heck sayin' to Atticus?

(*As they go inside, JEAN comes on. The lights begin slowly dimming, and an inner curtain is lowered. Then ATTICUS enters carrying a standing hat rack which he sets up, and over which he hangs the light bulb, the cord to which goes offstage. Then he sets up his folding chair beside this.*)

JEAN (*meanwhile*): Dill and I recounted all we'd heard of the conversation in the yard, and Jem thought about it. He hardly said a word through dinner. Then, later, instead of going to bed, Jem said he thought he'd go downtown for a while. I decided I was coming, too – and there was no stopping Dill.

(*The stage is now much darker.*)

JEAN: We crept past Mrs Dubose's house – the Radley place – and then on to the town square. It was deserted. We thought Atticus was probably in his office, and we went over – but he wasn't. We were getting uneasy.

(SCOUT, JEM *and* DILL *are coming on stage and they go a few steps past* JEAN, *not seeing her, and then stop.*)

JEAN: We came around by the courthouse and when we did, we noticed something peculiar – there was a light over the door to the jailhouse.

(ATTICUS *has meanwhile seated himself in his chair, opened his newspaper, and turned on the dim light bulb hanging beside him, and is reading.*)

JEM (*relieved*): There he is!
SCOUT (*starting*): Well, let's –
JEM (*grabbing her*): No, Scout.

Act I

SCOUT: I just want to ask why he's sitting in front of the jailhouse.

DILL: Maybe we shouldn't bother him right now.

SCOUT: But –

DILL: It's pretty late.

JEM: He's all right, so let's go home. I just wanted to see where he was.

(The sound of approaching cars is heard.)

SCOUT: After all this runnin' round town, we might at least –

JEM: Shh –

SCOUT: He can't hear me.

JEM: No – *listen*!

DILL: It's cars. A lotta cars coming.

(The sound is getting closer, and then it stops.)

JEM *(nervously)*: I wonder what –

DILL: So many.

JEM *(hushed; urgent)*: Get down. We'll get down 'n' watch.

(They get down to watch unseen. The stage light is quite dim now except for the small area around ATTICUS, who has meanwhile looked up at the sound. He closes his newspaper, folds it and puts it in his lap. Then he pushes his hat back on his head, waiting.)

SCOUT *(a half-scared whisper)*: What's happening?

JEM *(whispering back)*: Quiet!

JEAN: The way it looked to us, Atticus was quite calm. He seemed to be expecting exactly what was coming.

(In the darkness, a group of men come on, seen only dimly, moving slowly and deliberately toward ATTICUS. The group includes MR CUNNINGHAM and BOB EWELL; the rest of the 'mob' are not identifiable in the dim light; they are all dressed in farm clothes.

They are facing toward ATTICUS, *sullen, determined and ominous.*)

BOB EWELL: He in there, Mr Finch?

ATTICUS: He is, and he's asleep. Don't wake him up.

MR CUNNINGHAM: You know what we want. Step aside from the door, Mr Finch.

ATTICUS: You can turn around and go home again, Walter.

MR CUNNINGHAM: Won't do that.

ATTICUS (*pleasantly*): Might as well. Heck Tate's around somewhere.

BOB EWELL: The hell he is.

THIRD MAN: Heck's bunch's so deep in the woods, they won't get out till morning.

ATTICUS: Indeed? Why so?

THIRD MAN: Called 'em off on a snipe hunt.

BOB EWELL (*crowing*): Didn't you think o' that, Mr Finch?

ATTICUS: Thought about it, but didn't believe it.

MR CUNNINGHAM: Guess that changes things.

BOB EWELL: Oh, yes, it do!

ATTICUS (*getting up from his chair*): Do you really think so?

(*At this,* SCOUT *is getting up.* ATTICUS *and the group face each other.*)

JEAN: 'Do you really think so?' was a dangerous question from Atticus. I decided he was about to deal with somebody. This was too good to miss!

SCOUT: I'm gonna see –

(*She darts forward.*)

JEM (*after her; anxiously*): Scout! Wait!

(*But* SCOUT *rushes up through the group*)

SCOUT (*as she comes*): H – ey, Atticus!

ATTICUS (*startled; afraid for her*): Scout!

(JEM *and* DILL *are following into the circle of light.*)

JEM (*apologetic*): Couldn't hang onto her.
ATTICUS (*urgently*): Go home, Jem. Take Scout and Dill and go home.

(JEM *is looking at the group.*)

ATTICUS: Jem – I said, go home.
JEM (*back to* ATTICUS): Will you be coming with us?
ATTICUS: Son, I told you –

(*A big man grabs* JEM.)

BIG MAN: I'll send him home.
SCOUT: Don't you touch him!
BIG MAN: I'm telling you to –

(SCOUT *kicks the big man in the shins, and he cries out, letting go of* JEM *and hopping back into the group.*)

ATTICUS: That'll do, Scout. Don't kick folks.
SCOUT (*indignant*): But he –
ATTICUS: No, Scout.
SCOUT: Nobody gonna do Jem that way.
THIRD MAN: All right, Mr Finch, *you* get 'em outa here.
BOB EWELL: Give ya fifteen seconds.
JEM: I ain't going.
ATTICUS: *Please*, Jem, take them and go.
JEM (*grimly determined*): No, sir.

(*The crowd is stirring with impatience.*)

CROWD (*muttering; angry*): Had about enough – the kids are *his* worry – Can't stand around all night – come on – get 'em outa the way and –

(*The last speaker is interrupted as* SCOUT *thinks she recognises a man in front.*)

SCOUT: Mr Cunningham – that you? (*Coming closer*) Hey, Mr Cunningham.

(MR CUNNINGHAM *does not reply. The others are watching.* SCOUT *is more confused.*)

SCOUT: Don't you remember me? I'm Jean Louise Finch. You brought us a big bag of turnip greens, remember?
ATTICUS (*perplexed*): Scout –
SCOUT (*struggling for recognition*): I go to school with your boy, Walter. Well, he's your boy, ain't he? Ain't he, sir?

(MR CUNNINGHAM *is moved to a small nod.* SCOUT *is relieved.*)

SCOUT: *Knew* he was your boy. Maybe he told you about me – because I beat him up one time – but he was real nice about it. Tell Walter 'hey' for me, won't you?

(*There is no reply. She tries harder to break through this baffling lack of response.*)

SCOUT: My father was telling me about your entailment. He said they're bad.

(*The lack of response is getting more disturbing.*)

SCOUT: Atticus – I was just sayin' to Mr Cunningham that entailments are bad – but I remember you said not to worry – it takes long sometimes – but you'd all ride it out together.

(SCOUT *has come to a stop, looking out at the silent men. She swallows.*)

SCOUT: What is it? Can't anybody tell me? (*A plea*) Mr Cunningham – what's the matter?

(*Suddenly* MR CUNNINGHAM *puts his hands on both of* SCOUT's *shoulders.*)

MR CUNNINGHAM: Ain't nothin' the matter, little lady. An' I'll tell my boy you said 'hey.'

(*With this,* MR CUNNINGHAM *straightens up and waves his hand.*)

MR CUNNINGHAM (*with authority*): Let's clear out of here, boys.

(*There is a moment of hesitation.*)

MR CUNNINGHAM (*firmly*): We're goin' home.

(*With this, the men start moving off.*)

JEM (*hushed with astonishment*): They're goin'!
ATTICUS (*a bit astonished himself*): Looks that way.
SCOUT (*going up to him*): Atticus – can *we* go home now?

(ATTICUS *takes out a handkerchief with which he wipes his face, and then blows his nose.*)

ATTICUS (*nodding*): Yes. Looks like we can go home now.

(*There is the sound of cars starting up and driving away. They look toward the sound.*)

JEM: I thought Mr Cunningham was a friend.

ATTICUS: Still is. He just has his blind spots along with the rest of us.

JEM: But he was ready to hurt you.

ATTICUS: Because he was a part of a mob. But a mob's always made up of people, and Mr Cunningham's still a man. What you children did – you made him remember that.

(*A soft husky voice, that of* TOM ROBINSON, *calls from behind.*)

TOM (*from the darkness*): Mr Finch?

(*They turn toward the voice.*)

TOM: They gone?

ATTICUS: They're gone, Tom. They won't bother you any more.

TOM (*voice only*): Thank you, Mr Finch.

ATTICUS: We're going to have a busy time. Better get your sleep.

TOM (*wryly humorous*): You better get some sleep, too.

(ATTICUS *smiles as he gathers his things together*)

ATTICUS: That's my intention. Good night, Tom.

(DILL *has come up to* ATTICUS.)

DILL (*respectfully*): Can I carry the chair for you, Mr Finch?

(ATTICUS *considers this request then hands the folded chair to* DILL.)

ATTICUS: Why, thank you, son.

(DILL *is deeply pleased.*)

SCOUT (*drained*): I want to go home.

Act I

(ATTICUS *affectionately grips* JEM's *shoulder with one hand and* SCOUT's *with the other*)

ATTICUS: You two certainly don't mind very well.
SCOUT (*puzzled*): Atticus – what was it you said we did to Mr Cunningham?
ATTICUS: You made him stand in my shoes for a minute.

(*With this,* ATTICUS *reaches up and turns out the light bulb, and in the darkness they exit.*

Meanwhile, the only light on the stage is a dim spot on JEAN. *As she speaks, the light comes up on the rest of the stage as the courtroom is set up.*)

JEAN: The following Monday, Atticus told us to stay home, and for a while we did. People were streaming into town like it was Saturday. Seemed like the whole county was coming for Tom Robinson's trial.

(*Members of the cast – or stagehands – are moving on the basic props for the courtroom. The judge's bench and chair and a witness chair. There is a bench for witnesses, a small table and chair, and another table with two chairs. As the scene is played, the jury is considered to be out in the audience. As* JEAN *continues,* JUDGE TAYLOR *takes his place behind the bench.* HECK TATE *sits in the witness chair.* BOB EWELL *and* MAYELLA EWELL *sit on the bench, while* ATTICUS *and* TOM ROBINSON *sit at the table.* MR GILMER *is standing to the side of the witness chair.*

Spectators come on carrying small folding chairs which they set up and sit on to watch the trial: MISS CRAWFORD, MISS ATKINSON, NATHAN RADLEY *and* MR CUNNINGHAM. HELEN ROBINSON *sits by herself and away from the white spectators.*)

JEAN (*continuing during the above*): When Jem, Dill and I

49

reached the courthouse square, we found it covered with picnic parties. Apparently, the trial was to be a gala occasion. There was no room at the public hitching rail – mules and wagons were parked under every available tree. People were washing down biscuit and syrup with warm milk from fruit jars. Some were gnawing on cold chicken and cold fried pork chops. In the far corner of the square, the Negroes sat quietly in the sun, dining on sardines and crackers. At some invisible signal, they all got up and started into the courthouse. We didn't want Atticus to see us, so we waited. Then, there were no seats left. Reverend Sykes asked if we'd care to sit on the coloured side of the balcony. Jem said, 'Gosh, yes' and we went in with him.

(SCOUT, JEM *and* DILL *are coming on during this with* REVEREND SYKES, *and they sit with* HELEN ROBINSON. REVEREND SYKES *gives her a reassuring pat, but she just stares forward.*)

JEAN: By the time we got there the trial was already started. The prosecutor, a Mr Gilmer from Abbottsville, was taking testimony from Heck Tate.

(JEAN *steps offstage.*)

MR GILMER: In your own words, Mr Tate.

HECK (*replying to* MR GILMER): Well, I was called –

MR GILMER (*motioning toward the audience*): Could you say it to the jury, Mr Tate? Who called you?

HECK (*turning toward the audience*): I was fetched by Bob – by Mr Bob Ewell yonder, one night.

MR GILMER: What night, sir?

HECK: The night of November twenty-first. I was leaving my office to go home when B – Mr Ewell came in, very excited he was, and said, get to his house quick, some N–Negro'd attacked his girl.

Act I

(REVEREND SYKES *sighs.* HELEN ROBINSON *closes her eyes with pain.*)

MR GILMER: Did you go?

HECK: Certainly. Got in the car and went out as fast as I could.

MR GILMER: And what did you find?

HECK: Found her lying on the floor. She was pretty well beat up, but I heaved her to her feet and she washed her face in the bucket, and she said she was all right.

MR GILMER: Go on.

HECK: I asked her who hurt her and she said it was Tom Robinson.

(JUDGE TAYLOR *looks to* ATTICUS *expecting an objection, but* ATTICUS *just gives a slight shake of his head.* HECK *takes a breath.*)

HECK: Asked her if he beat her up like that; she said, yes, he had. Asked her if he took advantage of her and she said, yes, he did. I went down to Robinson's house and brought him back. She identified him as the one, so I took him in. That's all there was to it.

MR GILMER (*returning to his seat at the table*): Thank you.

JUDGE TAYLOR: Any questions, Atticus?

(ATTICUS *turns his chair to the side and crosses his legs.*)

ATTICUS (*leaning back*): Yes. Did you call a doctor, Sheriff?

HECK: No, sir.

ATTICUS (*with a slight edge*): Why not?

HECK: It wasn't necessary, Mr Finch. But she was mighty banged up.

ATTICUS: And you didn't –

JUDGE TAYLOR (*cutting in*): He's answered the question, Atticus.

ATTICUS (*smiling*): Just wanted to make sure, Judge. (*Turning to* HECK) Sheriff, you say she was mighty banged up. In what way? Just describe her injuries, Heck.

HECK: There was already bruises comin' on her arms, and she had a black eye startin'.

ATTICUS: Which eye?

HECK: Let's see – her left.

ATTICUS: Her left facing you, or her left looking the same way you were?

HECK (*thinking about it*): That'd make it her right. It was her right eye, Mr Finch. I remember now, she was banged up on that side of her face.

(ATTICUS *looks at* TOM, *then back at* HECK.)

ATTICUS (*demanding*): Please repeat what you said.

HECK: Her right eye.

ATTICUS: No – you said she was banged up on that side of her face. Which side?

HECK: The right side.

(REVEREND SYKES *and* HELEN *are whispering.*)

ATTICUS: That's all, Heck.

(HECK *steps down and walks over to the bench.*)

MR GILMER (*calling*): Robert Ewell.

(BOB EWELL *hops up and comes up to the witness chair. The* COURT CLERK *administers the oath.*)

CLERK: Swear to tell the truth, the whole truth, and nothing but the truth?

BOB EWELL (*crowing*): So help me God.

(MR GILMER *nods toward the chair;* EWELL *sits.*)

MR GILMER: Mr Robert Ewell?

BOB EWELL: That's m'name, cap'n.

(MR GILMER *does not particularly like* EWELL.)

MR GILMER: Are you the father of Mayella Ewell?
BOB EWELL: Well, if I ain't, I can't do anything about it now. Her ma's dead.
JUDGE TAYLOR (*firmly*): Are you the father of Mayella Ewell?
BOB EWELL (*cowed*): Yes, sir.
JUDGE TAYLOR: Get this straight. There will be no audibly obscene speculations on any subject from anybody in this courtroom. Do you understand?

(EWELL *nods.*)

JUDGE TAYLOR: All right, Mr Gilmer.
MR GILMER: Thank you, sir. Mr Ewell, tell us what happened on the evening of November twenty-first.
BOB EWELL: I was comin' in from the woods with a load o' kindlin' and just as I got to the fence, I heard Mayella screamin' like a stuck hog inside the house.
MR GILMER: What time was it, Mr Ewell?
BOB EWELL: Just 'fore sundown. Well, I was sayin', Mayella was screamin' like –

(*The* JUDGE *clears his throat, irritated, and* BOB EWELL *hesitates.*)

MR GILMER (*prodding*): Yes? She was screaming?
BOB EWELL: She was raising this holy racket so I dropped m' load and run as fast as I could up to the window – and I seen – I seen –

(*He gets up and points angrily at* TOM ROBINSON.)

BOB EWELL: I seen that black nigger yonder attackin' my Mayella!

(*There is a gasp from the spectators and a low moan from* HELEN ROBINSON. MR GILMER *is going up to the bench, where he speaks quietly to the* JUDGE. REVEREND SYKES *leans across to* JEM.)

REVEREND SYKES: Mr Jem. Take Miss Jean Louise home. Mr Jem, you hear me?

JEM (*turning to her*): Scout – go home. Dill, you 'n' Scout go home.

SCOUT: You can't make me.

JEM (*to* REVEREND SYKES): I think it's okay, Reverend. She doesn't understand.

SCOUT: I most certainly do. I can understand anything you can.

REVEREND SYKES (*disturbed*): This ain't fit for Miss Jean Louise – or you boys, either.

(REVEREND SYKES *and the other spectators, talking excitedly to each other, are interrupted by* JUDGE TAYLOR, *who is banging his gavel for attention.*)

JUDGE TAYLOR: Quiet! There has been a request that this courtroom be cleared of spectators, or at least of women and children – a request that for the time being will be denied. People generally see what they look for, and hear what they listen for. And they have the right to make whatever decisions they consider best for their children. You may feel there's something here to be learned. Or you may decide you do not wish to face this problem. It's up to you to make the decision. I suggest you do it right now. I'm interrupting this trial for a ten-minute recess.

(*The* JUDGE *bangs the gavel and rises. As he does, the curtain falls.*)

END OF ACT ONE

ACT TWO

(*Revealed is the trial scene with everyone back in place after the short recess declared by* JUDGE TAYLOR. BOB EWELL *is in the witness stand,* MR GILMER *stands near him waiting,* ATTICUS *sits at his table with* TOM ROBINSON, *and the spectators are seated, as before.*)

JUDGE TAYLOR (*looking about; dryly*): I see we still have a few with us. Well, let's get on.

(*He raps casually with his gavel and turns to* EWELL.)

JUDGE TAYLOR: Mr Ewell, you will keep your testimony within the confines of Christian English usage, if that's possible. (*Nods*) Proceed, Mr Gilmer.
MR GILMER (*uneasily*): Where we were – we were –
JUDGE TAYLOR (*to the point*): Mr Ewell, did you see the defendant attacking your daughter?
BOB EWELL: Yes, I did.
MR GILMER (*to the* JUDGE): Thank you, sir. (*To* EWELL) You said you were at the window?
BOB EWELL: Yes, sir.
MR GILMER: Did you have a clear view of the room?
BOB EWELL: Yes, sir.
MR GILMER: How did the room look?
BOB EWELL: All slung about, like there was a fight.
MR GILMER: What did you do when you saw the defendant?

BOB EWELL: I run around the house to get in, but he run out the front door just ahead of me. I sawed who he was, but I was too distracted about Mayella to run after him. Mayella was in there squallin', so I run in the house.

MR GILMER: Then what did you do?

BOB EWELL: I run for Heck Tate quick as I could. I knowed who it was all right, passed the house every day, lived down yonder in that nigger-nest. (*Turning to the* JUDGE) Jedge, I've asked this county for fifteen years to clean out that nest down yonder. They're dangerous to live around. (*Speaking as a 'put-upon' citizen*) 'Sides devaluin' my property.

MR GILMER (*wincing; hurriedly*): That's all. Thank you, Mr Ewell.

(*Well satisfied with himself,* EWELL *hops down, smiling as he goes. He bumps into* ATTICUS, *who is approaching. There is a stir of amusement which* EWELL *construes as approval.*)

ATTICUS (*meanwhile; genially*): Just a minute, sir. Could I ask you a question or two?

(EWELL *darts a glance at the* JUDGE, *who nods his head toward the witness chair.*)

BOB EWELL (*going back*): Sure – go ahead.

ATTICUS: Thank you, Mr Ewell. Folks were doing a lot of running that night. Let's see, you say you ran to the house, you ran to the window, you ran inside, you ran for Mr Tate. Did you, during all this running, run for a doctor?

BOB EWELL: Wadn't no need to.

ATTICUS: Didn't you think the nature of your daughter's injuries warranted immediate medical attention?

BOB EWELL: Never called a doctor in my life. If I had, would've cost me five dollars. That all the questions?

ATTICUS: Not quite. Mr Ewell, you heard the sheriff's testimony, didn't you?

BOB EWELL (*deciding it is safe to answer*): Yes.

ATTICUS: Do you agree with his description of Mayella's injuries? Her right eye blackened, that she was beaten around the –

BOB EWELL: Yeah. I hold with everything Tate said.

ATTICUS: He said her right eye was blackened.

BOB EWELL: I holds with Tate.

ATTICUS: Mr Ewell, can you read and write?

MR GILMER: Objection. Can't see what witness's literacy has to do with the case, irrelevant 'n' immaterial.

ATTICUS (*quickly*): Judge, if you'll allow the question, plus another one, you'll soon see.

JUDGE TAYLOR: All right. But make sure we see, Atticus. (*To* MR GILMER) Overruled.

ATTICUS (*to* EWELL): Will you write your name and show us?

BOB EWELL: I most positively will. How do you think I sign my relief checks?

(*There is an amused stir among the spectators.* ATTICUS *is taking an envelope from his pocket and then unscrewing his fountain pen.*)

SCOUT (*while this is happening; a worried whisper*): Jem – do you think Atticus knows what he's doin'?

JEM (*uncertainly*): *Seems* like he knows.

SCOUT: Far back as I c'n remember, he said never, never, never ask a question on cross-examination unless you already know the answer.

JEM (*he remembers, too*): 'Cause you might get an answer that'll wreck your case.

SCOUT (*watching again; nervously*): Looks to me like he's gone frog-sticking without a light.

(ATTICUS *has presented the envelope to* BOB EWELL, *shaken the fountain pen and given him that, too.*)

ATTICUS: Would you write your name for us? Clearly now, so the jury can see you do it.

(*With a flourish,* EWELL *finishes writing his name.*)

MR GILMER (*curiously*): What's so interestin'?

JUDGE TAYLOR: He's left-handed.

ATTICUS (*nodding*): That's it.

BOB EWELL (*outraged*): What's my bein' left-handed have to do with it? (*To* JUDGE TAYLOR) He's tryin' to take advantage of me. Tricking lawyers like Atticus Finch take advantage of me all the time with their tricking ways. But it don't change what I saw, and I'll say it again – I saw that nigger –

ATTICUS: That's all, Mr Ewell.

(*The furious little man is stalking back to his seat.*)

JEM (*meanwhile*): I think we've got him.

SCOUT: Don't count your chickens.

DILL (*hushed, eager*): Her *right* eye was blacked so it had to be someone left-handed.

SCOUT (*hushed in reply*): Maybe Tom Robinson's left-handed.

MR GILMER (*calling*): Mayella Violet Ewell.

(*As* MAYELLA *approaches, the* COURT CLERK *administers the oath.*)

CLERK: Swear to tell the truth, the whole truth and nothing but the truth.

MAYELLA (*nodding; softly*): Yes.

(MAYELLA *sits.*)

MR GILMER: Please tell the jury in your own words what happened on the evening of November twenty-first.

(MAYELLA *does not reply.*)

MR GILMER: Where were you at dusk on that evening?

MAYELLA: On the porch.

MR GILMER (*trying to prod her along*): What were you doing on the porch?

(MAYELLA *hesitates.*)

JUDGE TAYLOR: Just tell us what happened. You can do that, can't you?

(MAYELLA *does not reply.*)

JUDGE TAYLOR: What are you scared of?

(MAYELLA *whispers something to him from behind her hand.*)

JUDGE TAYLOR: What was that?

MAYELLA (*pointing at* ATTICUS): Him. Don't want him doin' me like he done Papa, makin' him out left-handed.

JUDGE TAYLOR (*perplexed*): How old are you?

MAYELLA: Nineteen and a half.

JUDGE TAYLOR: I see. Well, Mr Finch has no idea of scaring you, and if he did, I'm here to stop him. Now sit up straight and tell us what happened.

(MAYELLA *takes a breath, and starts nervously*)

MAYELLA: Well – I was on the porch and – and he came along and, you see, there was this old chiffarobe in the yard Papa'd brought in to chop up for kindlin'. Papa told me to do it while he was off in the woods, but I wasn't feelin' strong enough then, so he came by –

MR GILMER: Who is 'he'?

MAYELLA: That'n yonder. Robinson.

MR GILMER: Then what happened?

MAYELLA: I said, come here, boy, and bust up this chaffarobe for me, I gotta nickel for you. So he came in the yard an' I went in the house to get him the nickel. An' 'fore I knew it, he was at me. He got me 'round the neck. I fought, but he hit me agin and agin.

(*As* MAYELLA *collects herself*)

MR GILMER: Go on.

MAYELLA: An' he took advantage of me.

MR GILMER: Did you scream and fight back?

MAYELLA: Kicked and hollered loud as I could.

MR GILMER: Then what happened?

MAYELLA: Don't remember too good, but Papa came in the room and was hollerin' who done it? Then I sorta fainted, an' the next thing I knew Mr Tate was helpin' me over to the water bucket.

MR GILMER: You fought Robinson hard as you could – tooth and nail?

MAYELLA: I positively did.

MR GILMER: But he took advantage of you?

MAYELLA (*holding back a sob*): I already told ya.

MR GILMER: That's all for now. But stay here. I expect big, bad Mr Finch has some questions.

JUDGE TAYLOR (*primly*): State will not prejudice the witness against counsel for the defence.

(ATTICUS, *smiling, has risen. He opens his coat, hooks his thumbs in his vest and without looking directly at* MAYELLA, *speaks casually to her.*)

ATTICUS: Miss Mayella, I won't try to scare you for a while, not yet. Let's get acquainted. How old are you?

MAYELLA: Said I was nineteen, said it to the judge yonder.

ATTICUS: You'll have to bear with me, Miss Mayella. I can't remember as well as I used to. I might ask you things you've already said before, but you'll give me an answer, won't you? Good.

Act II

MAYELLA: Won't answer a word as long as you keep on mockin' me.

ATTICUS (*startled*): Ma'am?

MAYELLA: Long as you call me 'ma'am' and say 'Miss Mayella.' (*To* JUDGE TAYLOR.) I don't have to take his sass.

JUDGE TAYLOR: That's just Mr Finch's way. We've done business in this court for years and Mr Finch is always courteous. Atticus, let's get on – and let the record show that the witness has not been sassed.

ATTICUS: How many sisters and brothers have you?

MAYELLA: Seb'm.

ATTICUS: You the oldest?

MAYELLA: Yes.

ATTICUS: How long has your mother been dead?

MAYELLA: Don't know. Long time.

ATTICUS: How long did you go to school?

MAYELLA: Two year – three year – dunno.

ATTICUS: Miss Mayella, a nineteen-year-old girl must have friends. Who are your friends?

MAYELLA (*puzzled*): Friends?

ATTICUS: Don't you know anyone near your age? Boys – girls – just ordinary friends?

MAYELLA (*angry*): You makin' fun o' me again, Mr Finch?

ATTICUS: Do you love your father, Miss Mayella?

MAYELLA: Love him, whatcha mean?

ATTICUS: Is he good to you, is he easy to get along with?

MAYELLA: He does tollable 'cept when –

ATTICUS: Except when?

MAYELLA: I said he does tollable.

ATTICUS (*gently*): Except when he's drinking?

(*The question is asked so gently that in spite of herself,* MAYELLA *nods.*)

ATTICUS: When he's riled – has he ever beaten you?

(MAYELLA *looks around, startled.*)

JUDGE TAYLOR: Answer the question, Miss Mayella.

MAYELLA: My paw's never touched a hair o' my head –

(ATTICUS *considers her a moment.*)

ATTICUS: We've had a good visit, Miss Mayella. Now we'd better get to the case. You say you asked Tom Robinson to come chop up a – what was it?

MAYELLA: A chiffarobe, a old dresser.

ATTICUS: Was Tom Robinson well known to you?

MAYELLA: Whaddya mean?

ATTICUS: Did you know who he was, where he lived?

MAYELLA (*nodding*): I knowed who he was. He passed the house every day.

ATTICUS (*turning away; casually*): Was this the first time you asked him to come inside the fence?

(MAYELLA *jumps, looking about nervously.*)

ATTICUS: Was this –

MAYELLA: Yes, it was.

ATTICUS: Didn't you ever ask him to come inside the fence before?

MAYELLA (*ready now*): I did not. I certainly did not.

ATTICUS (*serenely*): You never asked him to do odd jobs for you before?

MAYELLA (*conceding*): I mighta.

ATTICUS: Can you remember any other occasions?

MAYELLA: No.

ATTICUS (*firmer*): All right, now to what happened. You said Tom Robinson got you around the neck – is that right?

MAYELLA: Yes.

ATTICUS: You say – 'he caught me and choked me and took advantage of me' – is that right?

MAYELLA: That's what I said.

ATTICUS: Do you remember him beating you about the face?

Act II

(MAYELLA *hesitates*.)

ATTICUS: You're sure enough he choked you. All this time you were fighting back, remember? You kicked and hollered. Do you remember him beating you about the face?

(MAYELLA *is looking about, uncertain how to reply*.)

ATTICUS: It's an easy question, Miss Mayella, so I'll try again. Do you remember him beating you about the face?

MAYELLA: No, I don't recollect if he hit me. I mean, yes, I do, he hit me.

ATTICUS: Was your last sentence your answer?

MAYELLA: Yes, he hit – I just don't remember – it all happened so quick!

JUDGE TAYLOR: Don't you cry, young woman.

ATTICUS: Let her cry if she wants to, Judge. We've got all the time in the world.

MAYELLA (*sniffing wrathfully*): Get me up here an' mock me, will you? I'll answer any questions you got.

ATTICUS: That's fine. There's only a few more. Will you identify the man who attacked you?

MAYELLA: I will. That's him right yonder.

ATTICUS: Tom, stand up. Let Miss Mayella have a good look at you. Is this the man, Miss Mayella?

(TOM *stands. He is a powerful young man, but his left hand is curled up and held to his chest.*)

JEM (*hushed*): Scout – Reverend – his left hand! He's crippled!

REVEREND SYKES (*whispering*): Caught in a cotton gin when he was a boy – like to bled to death. Tore all the muscles loose.

ATTICUS: Is this the man who attacked you?

MAYELLA: It most certainly is.

ATTICUS (*hard*): How?

MAYELLA (*raging*): I don't know how, but he did. I said it all happened so fast I –

ATTICUS: Let's consider this calmly.

MR GILMER: Objection. He's browbeating the witness.

JUDGE TAYLOR: Oh, sit down, Horace.

ATTICUS: Miss Mayella, you've testified the defendant choked and beat you. You didn't say he sneaked up behind you and knocked you cold. Do you wish to reconsider any of your testimony?

MAYELLA: You want me to say something that didn't happen?

ATTICUS: No, ma'am, I want you to say something that did happen.

MAYELLA: I already told ya.

ATTICUS: He hit you? He blacked your left eye with his right fist?

MAYELLA (*seeing the point*): I ducked and it – it glanced. That's what it did. I ducked and it glanced off.

ATTICUS: You're a strong girl. Why didn't you run?

MAYELLA: Tried to –

ATTICUS: And you were screaming all the time?

MAYELLA: I certainly was.

ATTICUS: Why didn't the other children hear you? Where were they?

(MAYELLA *makes no reply.*)

ATTICUS: Why didn't your screams make them come running?

(MAYELLA *makes no reply.*)

ATTICUS: Or didn't you scream until you saw your father in the window? You didn't scream till then, did you?

(MAYELLA *makes no reply.*)

ATTICUS: Did you scream at your father instead of Tom Robinson? Is that it?

(MAYELLA *makes no reply.*)

Act II

ATTICUS: Who beat you up? Tom Robinson or your father?

(MAYELLA *makes no reply.*)

ATTICUS: Miss Mayella – what did your father really see in that window?

(MAYELLA *covers her mouth with her hands.*)

ATTICUS: Why don't you tell the truth, child – didn't Bob Ewell beat you up?

(*With this,* ATTICUS *turns away, and lets out a breath. He looks a little as though his stomach hurts.* MAYELLA'*s face is a mixture of terror and fury.*)

MAYELLA (*gasping a quick breath and calling out*): I – I got somethin' to say.

(ATTICUS *walks back and sits wearily at his table.*)

ATTICUS (*with compassion*): Do you want to tell us what happened?

MAYELLA: I got somethin' to say an' then I ain't gonna say no more. That black man yonder took advantage of me an' if you fine fancy gentlemen don't wanta do nothin' about it then you're all yellow stinkin' cowards, stinkin' cowards, the lot of you. Your fancy airs don't come to nothin' – your ma'amin' and Miss Mayellarin' don't come to nothin', Mr Finch.

(MAYELLA *covers her face with her hands to hold back her sobs.*)

MR GILMER: That's all. (*Helping her out of the witness chair*) You can step down now.

65

(*As* MAYELLA *continues on to the bench to sit with her father,* MR GILMER *turns to* JUDGE TAYLOR)

MR GILMER: Sir – the State rests.

JUDGE TAYLOR: Shall we try to wind up this afternoon? How about it, Atticus?

ATTICUS: I think we can.

JUDGE TAYLOR: How many witnesses you got?

ATTICUS: One.

JUDGE TAYLOR: Well, call him.

ATTICUS (*rising*): I call Tom Robinson.

(TOM *rises and walks toward the witness chair. The* COURT CLERK *holds out the Bible to him.* TOM *cannot put his crippled left hand on the Bible, so he touches it with his right.*)

TOM: Sorry, sir.

JUDGE TAYLOR: That's all right, Tom.

CLERK: Do you swear the evidence you're about to give is the truth, the whole truth, and nothing but the truth?

TOM (*nodding*): I swear. (TOM *is motioned into the witness chair and he sits quietly and, naturally, afraid.*)

ATTICUS: You're Tom Robinson, twenty-five years of age, married with three children, and you've been in trouble with the law once before. A thirty-day sentence for disorderly conduct. What did that consist of?

TOM: Got in a fight with another man. He tried to cut me. But it wasn't much. Not enough to hurt.

ATTICUS: You were both convicted?

TOM (*nodding*): I had to serve 'cause I couldn't pay the fine. The other fellow paid his'n.

ATTICUS: Were you acquainted with Mayella Violet Ewell?

TOM: Yes, sir. I had to pass her place goin' to and from the field every day.

ATTICUS: Whose field?

TOM: I work for Mr Link Deas.

ATTICUS: You pass the Ewell place to get to work. Is there any other way to go?

TOM: No, sir, none's I know of.

ATTICUS: Tom, did she ever speak to you?

TOM: Why, yes, sir. I'd tip m'hat when I'd go by and one day she asked me to come inside the fence and bust up a chiffarobe.

ATTICUS: When did she ask you to chop up the – the chiffarobe?

TOM: Mr Finch, it was way last spring. After I broke it up she said 'I reckon I'll hafta give you a nickel, won't I' an' I said, 'No, ma'am, there ain't no charge.' Then I went home. That was way over a year ago.

ATTICUS: Did you ever go on the place again?

TOM: Yes, sir.

ATTICUS: When?

TOM: I went lots of times.

(There is a murmur among the spectators, and JUDGE TAYLOR *raps his gavel without comment.)*

ATTICUS: Under what circumstances?

(TOM does not quite understand.)

ATTICUS: Why did you go inside the fence lots of times?

TOM: She'd call me in. Seemed like every time I passed by yonder, she'd have somethin' for me to do – choppin' kindlin', totin' water for her.

ATTICUS: Were you paid for your services?

TOM: No, sir, not after she offered me a nickel the first time. But I was glad to do it. Mr Ewell didn't seem to help her none, and neither did the chillun, and I knowed she didn't have no nickels to spare.

ATTICUS: Where were the other children?

TOM: They were always around, all over the place.

ATTICUS: Would Miss Mayella talk to you?

TOM: Yes, sir, she talked to me.

ATTICUS: Did you ever – at any time – go on the Ewell property – did you ever set foot on the Ewell property without an express invitation from one of them?

TOM: No, sir, Mr Finch, I never did. I wouldn't do that, sir.

ATTICUS: Tom, what happened to you on the evening of November twenty-first?

(*The spectators draw in a collective breath and lean forward.*)

TOM: Mr Finch, I was goin' home as usual that evenin', and when I passed the Ewell place, Miss Mayella were on the porch, like she said she were. It seemed real quiet like, an' I didn't quite know why. She called to me to come there and help her a minute. Well, I went inside the fence an' looked for some kindlin' to work on, but I didn't see none, and she says 'Naw, I got somethin' for you to do in the house. Th' old door's off its hinges.' I said you got a screwdriver, Miss Mayella? She said she had. Well, I went up the steps and she motioned for me to come inside. (*Taking a breath*) I went in an' looked at the door. I said Miss Mayella, this door look all right. Those hinges was all right. Then she shet the door. Mr Finch, I was wonderin' why it was so quiet like, 'n it come to me that there weren't a chile on the place, not one of 'em, an' I said Miss Mayella, where the chillun?

(TOM *pauses to run his hand over his face.*)

ATTICUS (*quietly*): Go on, Tom.

TOM: I say where the chillun, an' she says – she was laughin' sort of – she says they all gone to town to get ice creams. She says, 'Took me a slap year to save seb'm nickels, but I done it. They all gone to town.'

(*Intensely uncomfortable and shifting in his seat,* TOM *stops.*)

ATTICUS: Tom, what did you say then?

TOM (*taking a breath*): I said somethin' like, why Miss Mayella, that's right smart o' you to treat 'em. An' she said 'You think so?' I don't think she understood what I was thinkin' – I meant it was smart of her to save like that, an' nice of her to treat 'em.

ATTICUS: I understand. Go on.

TOM: I said I best be goin', I couldn't do nothin' for her, an' she says oh yes I could, an' I ask her what, an' she says to just step on that chair yonder an' git that box down from on top of the chiffarobe.

ATTICUS: Not the same one you busted up?

TOM (*smiling*): No, sir, another one. Most as tall as the room. So I done what she told me, an' I was just reachin' when she – she grabbed me round the legs, Mr Finch. She scared me so bad I hopped down an' turned the chair over – that was the only thing, only furniture 'sturbed in that room, Mr Finch, when I left it. I swear 'fore God.

ATTICUS: What happened after you turned the chair over?

(TOM *has come to a stop, looking about the room nervously.*)

ATTICUS: Tom, you've sworn to tell the whole truth.

(TOM *still hesitates.*)

ATTICUS (*prodding*): What happened after that?

JUDGE TAYLOR: Answer the question.

TOM: When I got down offa that chair, she sorta – jumped at me.

ATTICUS: Jumped? Violently?

TOM: No, sir, she – she hugged me. She hugged me round the waist.

(*There's a growing murmur as the spectators react to each other at this. It is cut short by* JUDGE TAYLOR's *gavel.*)

ATTICUS: Tom – what did she do then?

TOM (*swallowing hard*): She says she never had her arms round a grown man before, an' she might as well start with me. She says 'Hug me back.' I say Miss Mayella lemme outa here an' I tried to run but she got her back to the door an' I'da had to push her. I didn't wanta harm her, Mr Finch, an' I say lemme pass, but just when I say it Mr Ewell yonder hollered through th' window.

ATTICUS: What did he say?

TOM: Somethin' not fittin' to say – not fittin' for these folks 'n' chillun to hear.

ATTICUS: Tom, you *must* tell the jury what he said.

TOM (*shutting his eyes*): He says you damn slut, I'll kill ya.

ATTICUS: Then what happened?

TOM (*opening his eyes again; unhappily*): I was runnin' so fast, Mr Finch, I didn't know what happened.

ATTICUS: Tom, did you attack Mayella Ewell?

TOM: I did not, sir.

ATTICUS: Did you harm her in any way?

TOM: I did not.

ATTICUS: Did you resist her advances?

TOM: Mr Finch, I tried to 'thout bein' ugly to her. I didn't wanta be ugly. I didn't wanta push her or nothin'.

ATTICUS: Let's go back to Mr Ewell. Who was he talking to?

TOM: He were talkin' and lookin' at Miss Mayella.

ATTICUS: Then you ran.

TOM: I sure did.

ATTICUS: Why did you run?

TOM: I was scared, sir.

ATTICUS: Why were you scared?

TOM: Mr Finch, if you was black like me, you'd be scared, too.

(ATTICUS *nods agreement with this, turns to* MR GILMER *as though saying 'Your witness,' and goes back to his chair.* MR GILMER *is rising and moving toward* TOM. *As this happens a*

VOICE *calls in – apparently from the spectators, but actually from offstage.*)

VOICE: I want the whole lot of you know one thing right now. Tom Robinson's worked for me eight years an' I ain't had a speck o' trouble outa him. Not a speck.

JUDGE TAYLOR (*rapping angrily with his gavel*): That's enough, Link Deas. If you have anything to say, you can say it under oath and at the proper time. (*To the jury*) You're to disregard the remark from Link Deas. (*Turning to* MR GILMER) Go ahead, Mr Gilmer.

MR GILMER: You were given thirty days for disorderly conduct, Robinson?

ATTICUS (*from his chair*): It was a misdemeanour and it's in the record, Judge.

JUDGE TAYLOR: Witness'll answer, though.

TOM: Yes, sir. I got thirty days.

(MR GILMER *looks significantly at the jury – the audience – then turns back to* TOM.)

MR GILMER: You're pretty good at busting up chiffarobes and kindling with one hand, aren't you?

TOM: Yes, sir. I reckon so.

MR GILMER: Strong enough to choke the breath out of a woman.

TOM: I never done that, sir.

MR GILMER: But you're strong enough?

TOM: I reckon so, sir.

MR GILMER: Had your eye on her for a long time, hadn't you, boy?

TOM: No, sir. I never looked at her.

MR GILMER: Then you were mighty polite to do all that chopping and hauling for her, weren't you, boy?

TOM: I was just tryin' to help out, sir.

MR GILMER: That was mighty generous of you. Why were you so anxious to do that woman's chores?

TOM (*hesitating*): Looked like she didn't have nobody to help her.

MR GILMER: With Mr Ewell and seven children on the place, boy?

TOM: Well, I says it looked like they never help her none.

MR GILMER: You did all this chopping and work from sheer goodness, boy?

TOM: Just tried to help her.

MR GILMER: You're a mighty good fellow, it seems – did all this for not one penny.

TOM: Yes, sir. I felt right sorry for her. She seemed to try more'n the rest of 'em.

MR GILMER (*he has got him*): *You* felt sorry for *her*! You felt *sorry* for her!

(*The spectators are shifting uncomfortably at this.*)

MR GILMER (*to the jury*): He felt sorry for her. (*Turning back to* TOM) Now you went by the house as usual last November twenty-first and she asked you to come in and bust up the chiffarobe?

TOM: No, sir.

MR GILMER: Do you deny you went by the house?

TOM: No, sir.

MR GILMER: She says she asked you to bust up the chiffarobe. Is that right?

TOM: No, sir, it ain't.

MR GILMER (*his tone is dangerous*): You say she's lying, boy?

(ATTICUS *is rising to protest, but* TOM *handles the question.*)

TOM: I don't say she's lying, Mr Gilmer. I say she's mistaken in her mind.

(ATTICUS *sits again. The light on the court scene begins to dim except for a spot light on* SCOUT, JEM *and* DILL *who is increasingly upset.*)

MR GILMER (*his tone rougher*): Tell me, boy. Why did you run away?

TOM: I was scared, sir.

MR GILMER: If you had a clear conscience, boy, why were you scared?

TOM: Like I says before, it weren't safe for any black man to be in a – fix like that.

MR GILMER (*sarcastically*): But you weren't in a fix. You testified you were resisting her advances. Were you scared she might hurt you – a big fellow like you?

TOM: No, sir. I was scared I'd be in court, just like I am now.

MR GILMER (*his voice rising*): Scared you'd have to face up to what you did?

TOM: No, sir. Scared I'd have to face up to what I didn't do.

MR GILMER: You bein' impudent to me, boy?

TOM: I didn't go to be.

(*The light on the court scene has now dimmed, but a spot of light remains on* SCOUT, JEM *and* DILL. DILL *has been so upset, he is not able to keep from crying. He is trying to disguise it, but* JEM *is aware of it.*)

JEM: Scout – go with Dill. Better take him outa here.

SCOUT: 'S the matter with him?

REVEREND SYKES: Might be a little thin-hided. I think you should go with him, Miss Jean Louise.

SCOUT (*getting up, but resentful*): Why me?

DILL (*with an effort*): I'm okay.

SCOUT (*taking his hand*): C'mon.

(*As* DILL *and* SCOUT *go, the light behind them dims.*)

SCOUT: The heat got you? Ain't you feeling good?

DILL (*getting himself in hand*): Said I was okay.

SCOUT: Wanta see something?

(*As* DILL *nods,* SCOUT *takes something from her pocket.*)

SCOUT: Look at these.

DILL (*examining them*): Two little statues – carved outa soap. Looks like a boy and a girl.

SCOUT: Got 'em from the knothole in the Radley tree.

(DILL *looks from the little figures to* SCOUT.)

DILL: Girl one could be you. Maybe the boy's Jem. Who carved 'em, you reckon?

SCOUT (*shrugging*): They was in the Radley tree.

(JEAN *comes on stage.*)

DILL (*considering*): I think I'm beginning to understand why Boo Radley stays shut up in that house – it's because he *wants* to stay inside.

SCOUT: That don't make any sense.

JEAN (*speaking to* SCOUT): Oh, yes, it does.

SCOUT (*apparently not aware of* JEAN, *but reacting to what she said; conceding*) Well, maybe.

DILL (*agreeing with her last comment*): Maybe he found out the way people can go outa their way to despise each other. (*Almost a cry*) Why'd Mr Gilmer have to do Tom Robinson that-away? Why'd he talk so hateful?

SCOUT: Dill, that's his job.

DILL: But he didn't have to sneer, and call him 'boy.'

SCOUT: That's just Mr Gilmer's way. They do all defendants that way, most lawyers, I mean.

DILL: Mr Finch doesn't.

SCOUT: He's not an example, Dill, he's – well, the same in the courtroom as he is at home – or on the street.

(DILL *nods patiently, making* SCOUT *speak with a slight edge.*)

SCOUT: Might be better if Atticus was a little more – if he was –

DILL (*exasperated*): Don't you realise yet – your father's not a run-of-the-mill man.

SCOUT (*dubiously*): Most people –

DILL (*cutting in with a snort*): Whatta you care about most people?

JEAN (*smiling*): You're expecting a lot from a very young girl, Dill.

DILL (*not noticing* JEAN; *speaking to* SCOUT): Maybe when you're older – when you've seen more of the world – this town even!

SCOUT (*not liking Dill's superiority*): If you've got over your cryin' fit, I guess I can take you back in.

DILL: Wasn't a cryin' fit. (*Going with her*) Just didn't like the way Mr Gilmer –

(SCOUT *and* DILL *return to their seats.*)

SCOUT (*with whispered superiority*): That's because you don't understand about the law.

(*The light is coming up on the trial area with everyone seated except* ATTICUS, *who stands by his table.*)

JEAN (*thoughtfully, as the light is coming up*): For an instant Scout and I almost together. I expect there's a little of the older woman already in every young girl – but they're not in touch very often. (*Considering the trial*) We only seem to grow up at special times – such as the time I walked back into that courthouse.

(SCOUT *punches* JEM *for attention.*)

SCOUT: His speech to the jury?

(JEM *nods.*)

SCOUT: How long's he been at it?

JEM: Just finished going over the evidence. An' Scout – we're gonna win! I don't see how we can't!

DILL (*suspiciously*): Did that Mr Gilmer –
JEM: Nothin' new. Just the usual. Hush now.

(ATTICUS, *who has paused by the table, has been unbuttoning his vest, unbuttoning his collar, and loosening his tie.*)

ATTICUS (*looking up to the* JUDGE): With the court's permission?

(JUDGE TAYLOR *nods, and* ATTICUS *takes off his coat and vest and puts them on his chair.*)

JEM (*startled*): Never saw him do that before.
SCOUT (*equally impressed*): Me either.

(*They are all leaning forward.* ATTICUS *looks directly out to the audience which is where the imaginary jury sits.*)

ATTICUS (*still at his table*): Gentlemen, this case is not a difficult one, it requires no minute sifting of complicated facts. This case is as simple as black and white.

(ATTICUS *moves slowly to the front of the stage.*)

ATTICUS: The state has not produced one iota of evidence that the crime Tom Robinson is charged with ever took place. It has relied instead upon the testimony of two witnesses – witnesses whose testimony has not only been called into serious question on cross-examination, but has been flatly contradicted by the defendant.

(ATTICUS *looks back at* MAYELLA.)

ATTICUS: I have nothing but pity in my heart for the chief witness for the state. But my pity does not extend to her putting a man's life at stake. And this is what she's done – done it in an effort to get rid of *her* guilt! I say guilt, because it was guilt that motivated her. She committed no crime, but she broke a rigid code of our society, a code so severe that whoever breaks it is hounded from our midst as unfit to live with. She's the victim of cruel poverty and ignorance, but she knew full well the enormity of her offence and she persisted in it.

(ATTICUS *pauses and takes a breath.*)

ATTICUS: She persisted and her subsequent reaction is something every child has done – she tried to put the evidence of her offence away, out of sight. What was the evidence? Not a stolen toy to be hidden. The evidence that must be destroyed is Tom Robinson, a human being. Tom Robinson, a daily reminder of what she did. What did she do? She tempted a Negro. She did something that in our society is unspeakable. She's white and she tempted a Negro. Not an old uncle, but a strong, young black man. No code mattered to her before she broke it – but it came crashing down on her afterwards! Her father saw what happened. And what did he do?

(ATTICUS *looks at* EWELL)

ATTICUS: There is circumstantial evidence to the effect that Mayella Ewell was beaten savagely by someone who led almost exclusively with his left hand.

(EWELL *rises, fists clenched.*)

BOB EWELL (*furious*): Damn you ta –

(JUDGE TAYLOR *raps sharply for order, and* HECK TATE *motions* EWELL *down while* ATTICUS *watches, unimpressed.*)

ATTICUS: Then Mr Ewell swore out a warrant, no doubt signing it with his left hand, and Tom Robinson now sits before you, having taken the oath with the only good hand he possesses – his right hand!

BOB EWELL (*back on his feet; raging*): You trickin' lyin' –

JUDGE TAYLOR (*rapping hard; angry*): Shut your mouth, sir, or you'll be fined for contempt!

(EWELL *is forced back into his seat by* HECK TATE)

ATTICUS: So a quiet, respectable Negro man who had the unmitigated temerity to feel sorry for a white woman is on trial for his life. He's had to put his word against his two white accusers. I need not remind you of *their* conduct here in court – their cynical confidence that you gentlemen would go along with them on the assumption – the evil assumption – that *all* Negroes lie, that *all* Negroes are basically immoral, an assumption one associates with minds of their calibre. However, you know the truth – and the truth is, *some* Negroes lie, and some Negro men are not to be trusted around women – black or white. And so with some white men. This is a truth that applies to the entire human race, and to no particular race.

(ATTICUS *pauses to clean his glasses with his handkerchief, speaking in a casual, lower key as he does so.*)

ATTICUS: In this year of grace, 1935, we're beginning to hear more and more references to Thomas Jefferson's phrase about all men being created equal. But we know that all men are *not* created equal – in the sense that some men are smarter than others, some have more opportunity because they're born with it, some men make more money, some ladies make better cakes, some people are born gifted beyond the normal scope –

(ATTICUS *puts his glasses back on. Speaking directly to the audience, he comes all the way down to the front of the stage. His manner has changed and he is speaking with controlled passion.*)

ATTICUS: But there's one way in which all men *are* created equal. There's one human institution that makes the pauper the equal of a Rockefeller, the stupid man the equal of an Einstein. That institution, gentlemen, is a court of law. In our courts – all men are created equal.

(ATTICUS *looks out at the imaginary jury for a moment and then continues, totally committed.*)

ATTICUS: I'm no idealist to believe so firmly in the integrity of our courts and in the jury system – that's no ideal to me, it is a living, working reality. But a court is only as sound as its jury, and a jury is only as sound as the men who make it up.

(ATTICUS *pauses to take a breath.*)

ATTICUS: I'm confident that you gentlemen will review without passion the evidence you've heard, come to a decision, and restore this defendant to his family. In the name of God, do your duty!

(ATTICUS *continues to look toward the front of the stage for a moment, then turns, walks back, and sits at the table with* TOM ROBINSON. *Nothing else happens on the stage until* ATTICUS *is seated. Then* SCOUT *reaches across and punches* JEM.)

SCOUT: Did he say somethin' else? As he was walkin' back?
JEM: I think he said – In the name of God, believe him!

(DILL *tugs at* SCOUT *and* JEM.)

DILL (*pointing*): Looka yonder!

(CALPURNIA, *carefully dressed, is coming shyly into the trial area. She pauses, waiting for recognition.*)

JUDGE TAYLOR (*becoming aware of her*): It's Calpurnia, isn't it?

CALPURNIA: Yes, sir. Could I speak to Mr Finch, please, sir? It hasn't got anything to do with – with the trial.
JUDGE TAYLOR (*nodding*): Of course.

(ATTICUS *is crossing over to her.*)

ATTICUS (*concerned*): What is it, Cal?

(CALPURNIA *is whispering to him quickly, and* ATTICUS *turns to* JUDGE TAYLOR)

ATTICUS: Judge – she says my children are missing, haven't turned up since noon. I – could you –
MISS STEPHANIE CRAWFORD (*calling*): They're up here, Atticus – (*Nodding*) Yonder.
ATTICUS (*calling*): Jem – Scout – come down. Meet me outside.

(ATTICUS *crosses to* JUDGE TAYLOR *and whispers something. The* JUDGE *nods, and* ATTICUS *crosses over to the children with* CALPURNIA *following. The light in the trial area dims. Meanwhile,* JEM, SCOUT *and* DILL *are coming over.*)

SCOUT (*to* JEM): Is he mad?
JEM (*shrugging*): We'll find out.

(ATTICUS, *exhausted, is approaching them, followed by the outraged* CALPURNIA. *The light on the trial area is now quite dim, though there is still a little light on the patient spectators.*)

SCOUT (*calling to him as he comes*): Hey, Atticus.
JEM (*excitedly*): We've won, haven't we, Atticus?
ATTICUS (*shortly*): I've no idea. You've been here all afternoon?

(*They nod.*)

ATTICUS: Well, go home with Calpurnia and stay home.

Act II

JEM: Aw, Atticus. Please let us hear the verdict.

ATTICUS: Have you done your reading today for Mrs Dubose?

JEM: Not today. *Please*, sir. We –

ATTICUS: Tell you what – you read to Mrs Dubose, eat your supper, and then Cal can bring you back.

CALPURNIA (*protesting*): Sir?

ATTICUS: They've heard it all up to now! They might as well hear the rest.

DILL: Suppose the jury comes back before –

ATTICUS: Probably will. They might be out and back in a minute.

JEM: You think they'll acquit him that fast?

ATTICUS (*quietly*): Go do your reading, eat your supper, and if the jury is still out when you get back, you can wait up there with Cal and hear the verdict. (*Deeply appreciative*) Thank you, Cal.

(ATTICUS *turns and walks off into the darkness of the trial area.*

JEAN *is coming on stage and the remaining light on the stage is dimming except for that on her. As the light on them is dimming,* CALPURNIA *starts to herd* JEM, SCOUT *and* DILL *offstage.*)

CALPURNIA (*indignantly*): I should skin every one of you alive! The very idea – you children listening to all that! Mister Jem, don't you know better 'n to take your little sister to that trial? As for you, Mister Dill, you watch out your aunt doesn't ship you back to Meridian first thing in the mornin'! You oughta be perfectly ashamed of yourselves!

(*The light on them should have dimmed by now.*)

JEAN: Calpurnia didn't stop expressing her outrage all the way home. When Jem ran over to read to Mrs Dubose, Cal worked over Dill and me.

(*The light begins coming up again, revealing the same group, but*

they have now turned around and are heading back, with CALPUR-
NIA *following.*)

JEAN: And she was still upset as we finished supper and
started back to the trial – wondering what on earth we'd
find.

CALPURNIA (*her voice dropping as they get closer*): Thought you
was gettin' some kinda head on your shoulders, Mister
Jem. Ain't you got any sense at all?

JEM: Don't you want to hear what happened?

CALPURNIA (*an angry whisper as they go to their seats*): Hush
your mouth, sir. If Mr Finch don't wear you out, I will!

DILL (*looking to the front of the stage with glad surprise*): The jury's
still out!

JEM (*looking about as he sits*): Nobody's moved hardly.

(*The light on the trial area should not come up yet, but it will be at
least partially visible from the spill of light illuminating the spectators.* JUDGE TAYLOR *is sitting where he was, his head on his
hand, half asleep.* MR GILMER *sits at his table going over some
notes.* MAYELLA *still sits on her bench, but* BOB EWELL *is not
there.* ATTICUS *is also offstage, as is* HECK TATE *and* TOM ROBIN-
SON. *The spectators are all in place except* MR CUNNINGHAM.)

REVEREND SYKES (*meanwhile; to* JEM): They moved around
some when the jury went out.

JEM: How long have they been out?

REVEREND SYKES: 'Bout an hour. Mr Finch and Mr Gilmer did
some more talkin' and Judge Taylor charged the jury.

(MR CUNNINGHAM *is coming back to his seat. He sits and
whispers into* NATHAN RADLEY's *ear. He whispers to* MISS
STEPHANIE *and she whispers to* MISS MAUDIE. *Meanwhile the
conversation between* REVEREND SYKES *and* JEM *continues.*)

DILL: How was he?

REVEREND SYKES: I'm not complainin' one bit. He was mighty fair-minded. I thought he was leanin' a little to our side. Made Mr Ewell so mad, he stamped out of the room.

JEM: The judge isn't supposed to lean either way. 'Sides, we don't need it 'cause we won anyway. I don't see how any jury –

REVEREND SYKES (*interrupting*): Don't be so confident, Mister Jem. I've never seen *any* jury decide in favour of a black man over a white man.

JEM: This case is different. (*Noticing the whispering*) What's all the whispering?

SCOUT (*concerned*): Must be somethin'.

(*At this,* BOB EWELL, *very full of himself at this moment, walks on stage, and crosses to sit with* MAYELLA. *He whispers to her, quite proud of himself. The trial area, however, is only partially lighted.*)

DILL (*uneasy*): That Bob Ewell looks mighty pleased 'bout somethin'.

SCOUT (*more concerned*): Wonder where's Atticus.

(*There is no answer to this, and they look forward, waiting. Then* JEAN *speaks, and as she does,* MISS MAUDIE *leans across the space between them to whisper something to* SCOUT.)

JEAN: We found out about the whispering. Atticus had been standing at the window at the end of the corridor outside and Bob Ewell came up to him, cursed him, told him he'd kill him if it took him the rest of his life, and when Atticus just stood there looking at him, Bob Ewell spat in his face.

(SCOUT *has turned, aghast, to whisper to* JEM *and* DILL.)

JEAN: According to what we heard, Atticus didn't bat an eye – just took out a handkerchief and wiped his face.

(*At this point,* ATTICUS, *pale but calm, his hands in his pockets, strolls on stage, crosses to his table and sits.* BOB EWELL *nudges his daughter and gestures for her to look at* ATTICUS. *However, he ignores them.*)

SCOUT (*whispering unhappily to* JEM): How could he let Ewell get away with a thing like that?

JEM (*just as unhappy*): Dunno.

SCOUT (*a hushed protest*): But he's a dead shot –

DILL (*defensively*): That's not his way –

SCOUT: I'm gonna ask him about this.

JEAN: But his only comment – all he said – 'I wish Bob Ewell wouldn't chew tobacco'.

(*They are all waiting.*)

JEAN (*quietly*): Several hours went by – and we waited. I don't think anyone expected the jury to be out so terribly long.

SCOUT: Jem – ain't it a long time?

JEM (*pleased*): Sure is, Scout.

JEAN: My brother thought it a favourable indication. Meanwhile, nobody moved about. Nobody left. (*Taking a breath*) Then, suddenly it was happening!

(HECK TATE *has come on stage during this last speech, and he pauses there, his voice ringing with authority. Light is coming up fully now on the trial area.*)

HECK: This court will come to order.

(HECK *steps back offstage again.* JUDGE TAYLOR *is rousing himself to sudden alertness, as is everyone else.* HECK *reappears quickly, escorting* TOM ROBINSON *to the table where* ATTICUS *waits.*)

HELEN (*an involuntary call as her husband crosses to the table*): Tom –

(TOM *looks at her, then turns away quickly to sit beside* ATTICUS.)

Act II

REVEREND SYKES (*gently*): Helen – you promised.

HELEN (*protesting*): Reverend – (*But she stops herself: agreeing in a low voice*) I promised.

(JEM *looks out to the front of the stage, meanwhile.*)

JEM (*with growing dismay*): Scout – Look. Look at the jury comin' in!

(JEM's *voice is making* DILL *nervous; he is also looking towards the front.*)

DILL: What about 'em?

SCOUT (*as she realises; hushed*): They're *not* looking at the defendant!

DILL (*more nervous*): What does it mean?

HECK (*calling*): The defendant will rise.

(*As* TOM *and* ATTICUS *are rising,* HECK *comes down to the front of the stage for an instant, turns and goes back to hand a slip of paper to* JUDGE TAYLOR.)

DILL (*as this is happening; a frantic whisper*): What's it mean, Scout?

SCOUT (*miserable*): You're gonna see.

DILL: See what?

JEM: Hush.

(JUDGE TAYLOR *has read the slip of paper. He suddenly seems very tired. He picks up his gavel, ready to rap with it, but sees it is not necessary. He leans forward.*)

JUDGE TAYLOR: The jury finds the defendant – guilty.

(*There is a sigh from some, an intake of breath from others, and a low moan from* HELEN. TOM *turns to look at her. The* JUDGE *is about to rap with his gavel, but decides against it again. Wearily, he tosses the gavel onto the table, leans back and nods to* HECK.)

HELEN (*not quite out loud, her lips forming his name*): Tom – Tom –

(ATTICUS *has put a hand on* TOM'S *shoulder and is speaking earnestly into his ear as* HECK TATE *approaches.* ATTICUS *then steps aside and* HECK *escorts* TOM *offstage.* BOB EWELL, *muttering disdainfully past the* JUDGE, *goes offstage followed by* MAYELLA. MR GILMER *also goes offstage, as does* JUDGE TAYLOR. *The reactions below are expressed during this and follow as quickly as the verdict registers.*)

SCOUT (*in shock*): We lost! It's all lost!

JEM (*heartbroken*): How could they find him guilty?

CALPURNIA (*an unhappy protest voiced mainly to herself*): Not right you children should see such things! Not right *any* children should see such things!

DILL (*hushed*): What happens now? What can we do?

JEM (*bitterly*): If the evidence don't matter, I don't see there's anything –

DILL (*whispered horror*): But they're not going to hurt Tom Robinson? Your father'll do something. Mr Finch won't let 'em. He'll – he –

(DILL *is stopped by* REVEREND SYKES' *hand on his shoulder, and as he looks back, he sees that the* REVEREND, HELEN *and* CALPURNIA *are standing respectfully. He realises, and rises to his feet as does* JEM. *Meanwhile* ATTICUS *has been left alone in the trial area. He has put some papers in his briefcase, slung his coat over his shoulder, and, utterly exhausted, he is collecting himself, unaware of the others.*)

SCOUT (*continuing meanwhile, her fists clenched, and leaning forward*): They c'n spit in his face, and find Tom Robinson guilty! But no matter what any of 'em says – Atticus – he's –

REVEREND SYKES (*his hand on her shoulder now*): Miss Jean
    Louise –

(*Interrupted*, SCOUT *turns to see them standing.* MISS MAUDIE
ATKINSON *is also standing to show her respect. The other white
spectators who have started moving offstage, carrying their chairs,
pause now, possibly out of curiosity, but they are also standing.*
ATTICUS *takes a breath, and walks offstage.*)

REVEREND SYKES: Miss Jean Louise – stand up. Stand up –
    your father's passing.

(SCOUT *gets to her feet with the others as her father continues
going offstage. As this is happening, the lights dim everywhere
except on* JEAN. REVEREND SYKES *helps* HELEN *off, while the
others take off the set pieces used for the trial scene, and the set,
while not yet lighted, is as it was earlier in the play. As this is
happening,* JEAN *is speaking, beginning as* ATTICUS *completes his
exit.*)

JEAN (*looking after her father*): When we spoke to Atticus later,
    Jem started to cry. He wanted to know how the jury could
    do it.

(JEAN *turns to the front of the stage.*)

JEAN: I'd never seen my father so close to being bitter. 'I don't
    know how,' he told us, 'but they did it. They've done it
    before, and they did it today and they'll do it again. And
    when they do it – seems only children weep.' (*Taking a
    breath*) As for Bob Ewell, he walked out of the courtroom
    expecting to find himself the town hero, but it turned out
    only a few really believed him – Atticus had destroyed his
    last shred of credibility. All Ewell got for his pain was –
    was, okay, we convicted the Negro, but now you – you get
    back to your dump. Ewell started making terrible threats.

This time we should have believed him. This time he was telling the truth.

(SCOUT *has come on stage and looks about.*)

JEAN: I hurried home ahead of Jem and Dill. I didn't want them to see me going back to the knothole in the tree. I'd put a note there thanking whoever it was who left me the nice surprises.

(SCOUT *is crossing quickly to the tree, and reaching up.*)

JEAN: I thought there might be an answer. What I found –
SCOUT (*as she touches it; with dismay*): Cement! Someone filled it with cement!

(NATHAN RADLEY *is strolling on stage, not yet seen by* SCOUT.)

NATHAN (*to her back, dryly*): Anything the matter?
SCOUT (*startled, whirling around*): What? (*Collecting herself*) No – nothing the matter. (*Half a question*) There's cement in the knothole.

(JEAN *goes offstage.*)

NATHAN (*nodding*): I filled it up.
SCOUT (*it takes courage to ask*): Why'd you do that, sir?
NATHAN: Tree's dying. You plug 'em with cement when they're sick. (*Going towards his house*) You ought to know that, Miss Jean Louise.
SCOUT (*after him*): The tree don't look sick to me.

(*But* NATHAN RADLEY *continues on into the house, shutting the door.*)

(JEM *and* DILL *are coming on stage.*)

SCOUT (*muttering to herself*): Whoever carved the soap statues, it wasn't him.

JEM (*to* SCOUT): Why'd you run ahead? Scared of old Mr Ewell?

SCOUT: Not one bit.

JEM: Why should he stand outside the courthouse talkin' so mean? His side won.

(MISS STEPHANIE CRAWFORD *is coming on stage.*)

DILL (*too much to bear*): But he hasn't won *really*. We can still do *something*?

JEM (*bitterly*): Looks to me like the minute Mayella Ewell opened her mouth and screamed, Tom Robinson was a dead man!

DILL (*shocked protest*): *Jem!*

MISS STEPHANIE (*bustling over*): I'm absolutely surprised at you children. Did Atticus give you permission to go to court?

(JEM *shrugs in reply.* MISS MAUDIE ATKINSON *is coming on stage.*)

MISS STEPHANIE: Why were you sitting over in the coloured balcony? Several people mentioned it. Wasn't it right close over there?

MISS MAUDIE (*disgusted*): Hush, Stephanie.

MISS STEPHANIE (*turning*): Do *you* think it's wise for children to –

MISS MAUDIE (*interrupting*): We've made the town this way for them. They might as well learn to cope with it.

MISS STEPHANIE: Least they don't have to wallow in it.

MISS MAUDIE (*tartly*): What happened in court is as much a part of Maycomb as missionary teas.

MISS STEPHANIE (*going up onto her porch*): Well – excuse me. Don't suppose they understood anyway.

(MISS STEPHANIE *pauses before going in, and speaks with what may be genuine sympathy.*)

MISS STEPHANIE: Too bad you had to see your daddy get beat.

(*With this,* MISS STEPHANIE *goes in.* JEM *and* SCOUT *are hurt by her comment, as is* DILL.)

DILL (*beginning softly*): When I get grown, I think I'll be a clown.

JEM (*not quite focusing*): What, Dill?

DILL: Yes, sir, a clown. There ain't one thing in this world I can *do* about folks, so I'm gonna join the circus and laugh my head off.

JEM: You've got it backwards, Dill. Clowns are sad. It's folks that laugh at them.

DILL: I'm gonna be a new kind of clown. I'm gonna stand in the middle of the ring and laugh – laugh in their faces!

(MISS MAUDIE *has been watching, disturbed by their unhappiness.*)

MISS MAUDIE: Don't pay attention to what *she* says about Atticus.

JEM: What do you mean?

MISS MAUDIE: I simply would like you to know that there are some men in this world who were born to do our unpleasant jobs for us. Your father's one of them.

JEM: Oh – well –

MISS MAUDIE: Don't you 'oh well' me, sir. You're just not old enough to appreciate what I said.

JEM (*troubled*): I always thought Maycomb folks were the best folks in the world.

MISS MAUDIE: We're the safest folks in the world. We're so rarely called on to be Christians, but when we are, we've got men like Atticus to go for us.

JEM: Who feels that way 'sides you?

MISS MAUDIE: The handful of people in this town who say that fair play isn't marked 'White Only.'

JEM (*must know*): But who? Who did one thing to help Tom Robinson?

MISS MAUDIE: His friends, for one thing, and people like us. We exist, too. People like Judge Taylor. People like Heck Tate. Start using your head, Jem. Did it ever strike you that Judge Taylor naming Atticus to defend Tom was no accident? That Judge Taylor might have had his reasons?

SCOUT: S'right, Jem. Usually the court appoints some new lawyer – one who is just startin'.

MISS MAUDIE: You're beginning to realise! A little more to it than you thought! (*Pressing*) Whether Maycomb knows it or not, we're paying your father the highest tribute we can pay a man. We trust him to do right.

SCOUT: Then why did he get beat?

MISS MAUDIE (*snorting*): Miss Stephanie talks nonsense. Maybe he didn't get an acquittal, but he got something. I was sitting in court waiting, and as I waited, I thought – Atticus Finch won't win, he can't win, but he's the only man in these parts who can keep a jury out so long in a case like this. And I thought to myself, take note of this time and this place. It's 1935 and it's Maycomb, Alabama, and we're making a step – it's just a baby-step, but it's a step.

(JEM, SCOUT *and* DILL *are looking at* MISS MAUDIE *and thinking about what she has just said. She takes a breath and collects herself.*)

MISS MAUDIE: I'm going into my kitchen now, and I'm going to make a cake. And I'd be pleased if you'd all come over later and have some of my cake.

SCOUT (*subdued*): Yes, Miss Maudie.

JEM: Thank you.

MISS MAUDIE: Mister Dill?

DILL (*half jumping*): Yes – I'll come. Thank you.

(*With this* MISS MAUDIE *goes up and enters her house.*)

DILL: I better stop over to Aunt Rachel. (*Pauses. Considering*) They trust him to do right. (*But this is too much for right now. He'll think about it some other time. Suddenly brightening*) I'll be back – and then we'll all have cake.

(*With this,* DILL *runs off.* SCOUT *takes* JEM's *hand and they go into the house. As* SCOUT *and* JEM *are going,* JEAN *comes back on stage.*)

JEAN: Tom Robinson was taken to the Enfield Prison Farm, about seventy miles away. Atticus thought Tom had a good chance for a new trial, but Tom just couldn't hope any more. His old employer made a job for Helen so she could support the children, but she had to pass the Ewell place and they shouted and chucked things at her. She was terrified till Heck Tate went out and made them desist. Then Ewell's threats got worse. Partly he blamed Judge Taylor, but the main focus of his sick fury was Atticus. The only man in Maycomb ever to be fired from the WPA for laziness was Ewell, and somehow he twisted that onto Atticus, too – said Atticus had got his job. It looked to us that it was building to a blow-up, but Atticus just went about his business – working on Tom's appeal. Then suddenly death was among us.

(JEM *has come out of the house as* CALPURNIA *is coming out of* MRS DUBOSE's *house, and they meet in the yard.*)

JEAN: First it was Mrs Dubose. Jem had started over to read to her, when he was stopped by Cal, who'd gone over to lend a hand. The doctor had just told her that Mrs Dubose had passed away.

Act II

(SCOUT *and* ATTICUS *are coming onto the porch, looking at* CAL-PURNIA *and* JEM, *who are approaching.*)

JEAN: And Jem found out why he'd been reading to her. She'd been given morphine for her pain, and she'd become an addict – but she wanted to break herself of it before she died. She wanted to leave the world beholden to nobody and nothing. Jem's reading was a distraction. It was a help.

JEM (*looking up at* ATTICUS): That's why you said I had to read to her?

(BOB EWELL, *whittling a piece of wood with a knife, is coming slowly on stage. He is full of a private joke that gives him a momentary sense of superiority.*)

ATTICUS (*nodding*): Her views on a lot of things were quite different from mine, but I was glad she asked you to read to her because I wanted you to see –

BOB EWELL (*cutting in*): Hello, Finch.

(ATTICUS *looks at him, then turns back to* JEM.)

ATTICUS (*continuing*): I wanted you to see what *real* courage is.

BOB EWELL (*gloating*): Got some good news, Finch.

ATTICUS (*glancing at* EWELL): Courage isn't a man with a knife in his hand. Jem – it's when you know you're licked before you begin, but you begin anyway and you see it through no matter what. You rarely win – but *sometimes* you do. Mrs Dubose won, all ninety-eight pounds of her!

BOB EWELL: Don't 'cha wanta hear, Finch?

(HELEN ROBINSON, *distraught, hurries on stage.*)

HELEN: Mr Finch – Cal – please –

ATTICUS (*coming down off the porch*): What is it? What's wrong, Helen?

(HECK TATE *is coming on stage quickly*.)

HECK (*calling*): Atticus –
ATTICUS: Cal –

(CALPURNIA *puts an arm around* HELEN.)

CALPURNIA (*anxiously*): One of the children?

(HELEN *can hardly talk*.)

HELEN: It's not the children –
ATTICUS (*to* HECK): What is it?
BOB EWELL (*getting back at them*): I'll tell you – they shot that nigger!
HECK (*ignoring* EWELL): Tom's dead!
HELEN: Mr Finch – they shot Tom!
ATTICUS: Heck?
HECK (*nodding*): He was running. It was during their exercise period. They said he just broke into a blind raving charge at the fence and started climbing over – right in front of them.
ATTICUS: Oh, my God! (*Turning to* CALPURNIA) Cal, please, take Helen inside. You children go inside.
BOB EWELL: They put seventeen bullet holes in him.
ATTICUS (*to his numb children*): I said for you to go inside.

(ATTICUS *turns to* HECK; *he does not see that the children are not moving*.)

ATTICUS: Didn't they try to stop him? Didn't they give him any warning?
HECK (*nodding*): They shouted, and then they fired a few shots in the air. They didn't shoot at him till he was almost over the fence.
HELEN: Mr Finch – how could they shoot *Tom*?
ATTICUS (*with difficulty*): Helen – to them he was just an escaping prisoner. He wasn't Tom to them.

94

HELEN (*bewildered*): Why didn't he wait for the appeal?

ATTICUS: I don't know. I told him we had a chance, but I couldn't say we had more than a chance. I guess Tom was fed up with white men's chances.

BOB EWELL: Ain't it just like a nigger to cut 'n' run?

CALPURNIA (*firmly*): You come inside, Helen.

(ATTICUS *turns to address* BOB EWELL *directly; he is barely able to control his anger.*)

ATTICUS: Do you have anything more you want to say, Mr Ewell?

(EWELL *starts to go, then stops, overwhelmed with spite.*)

BOB EWELL: Yes – I say there's one down –

(*With his knife,* EWELL *slashes a piece from his whittling.*)

BOB EWELL: – two to go! Now guess who's gonna be next!

(BOB EWELL *slashes another piece from his whittling and walks offstage.*)

HECK (*thoughtfully*): I think I'd keep a shotgun loaded with double O.

JEM (*from the porch*): He doesn't have a shotgun.

ATTICUS: I can't believe Bob Ewell would ever really come after me. But if he should, I'll deal with him.

HECK (*considering*): I expect you would.

ATTICUS (*dropping his voice*): Was Tom really shot up that much?

HECK (*unhappily*): There's talk, but I don't know. You better be careful, Atticus.

ATTICUS (*after him*): Sure – thanks, Heck.

JEM (*firmly*): Atticus, I'm worried about you. And I think you should get a gun.

ATTICUS: I told you twice to go inside. Let's all go and be with Helen.

(*They start to go in.*)

ATTICUS (*pointedly*): And remember – she's someone who's heard enough about guns.

(*As they go into the house, the light begins to dim except for a small isolated light on* JEAN. *As she speaks, the light continues to dim until the stage is entirely dark except for her, and she is only dimly seen.*)

JEAN: Atticus was underestimating what anger and sick frustration could do to an already unbalanced man. The night we found out – there was a pageant at the school auditorium and Jem said he'd take me. It was to be our longest journey together. Wind was coming up and Jem said it might be raining before we got home. Heavy clouds had blacked out the moon, and it was pitch dark. Before we left, Cal had a pinprick of apprehension. When I asked what was the matter, she said 'Somebody just walked over my grave.' On the way to school, Jem had a flashlight.

(*At this,* JEM *turns on a pinpoint flashlight, directing it into* SCOUT's *face.*)

JEM (*teasing*): You scared? Scared of haints?
SCOUT (*scornfully*): Haints, hot steams, incantations, secret signs – I'm too old.
JEM (*reciting*): 'Angel bright, life-in-death, get off the road, don't suck my breath.'
SCOUT (*sharply*): Cut it out!
JEM: You're scared now because we're passin' Boo Radley's place.
SCOUT: I'm *not* scared. 'Sides he must not be home.

JEM: How c'n ya tell?

SCOUT (*logically*): If he was, there wouldn't be a bird singing in the Radley tree. Hear that mocker?

(*As they listen to the birdsong, the flashlight goes out.*)

SCOUT: Turn on your light again.

JEM: Somethin' wrong with it. C'mon. Gimme your hand.

(*They start to go.*)

SCOUT: How do you know where we're at?

JEM: I can tell we're under the tree now because we're passing through a cool spot. (*As they are going offstage*) Careful.

JEAN: The trip back from the pageant was more eventful. The moon had been in and out of the heavy rainclouds, but as we started home it was black dark – and there was the still-ness that sometimes comes before a thunderstorm. (*Her voice becoming increasingly involved*) Jem thought he heard something, and we stopped to listen. Then we walked a few more steps, and he stopped again. I thought he was trying to scare me, but that wasn't it. He held my hand tight and pulled me along fast. Then we stopped suddenly.

(*There are sounds of several steps being taken, and then they stop.*)

JEAN: I thought I heard steps following, too.

(*There is a rumble of distant thunder. SCOUT speaks to JEM in the darkness. The light on JEAN has dimmed away. The stage is in total darkness.*)

SCOUT (*voice in the darkness*): Jem, are you afraid?

JEM (*voice*): Think we're not too far to the tree now.

SCOUT: Reckon we ought to sing, Jem?

JEM (*worried*): No. Be real quiet, Scout.

(*There is another rumble of thunder.*)

SCOUT: Just the thunderstorm gettin' closer.
JEM (*more worried*): No, not that – Listen!

(*There is the sound of someone running toward them.*)

SCOUT (*with sudden alarm*): I hear! Jem!
JEM (*shouting imperatively*): He's coming! Run, Scout! Run!
   Run!
SCOUT (*in trouble*): I tripped! Jem – help me!
JEM (*frantic*): Where are ya? Scout – C'mon!
SCOUT (*growing panic*): Can't see! I don't know where –
JEM: Get away, Scout – *Run!*

(*Then* JEM *cries out as someone grabs him. There is a sound of struggling. A man's voice is heard – angry, unintelligible.*)

ATTACKER: Got 'cha – now you'll – damn ya – show 'em

(*There is a crack and* JEM *screams with pain.*)

SCOUT (*hushed terror*): Jem! (*A cry*) Help us – someone – *help!*

(*The blackness is split as the Radley door is suddenly swung wide open, the light from inside silhouetting a big* MAN *in the doorway. There may be a clap of thunder accompanying this action. The light may briefly reveal a man standing over* JEM *on the ground, and struggling with the stricken* SCOUT. *The less seen the better. The light is quickly cut off as the* MAN *slams the door behind him and joins the struggle in the darkness. There is a moment of continued struggle, grunts, Scout's sobs, and then a man's cry of pain: 'Ahhhh!'*

The sounds of struggle stop. JEM *is picked up by the* MAN *from the Radley house and carried to the Finch house, where the porch light is turned on, and* ATTICUS *comes out.* JEM's *arm is hanging as though broken.* SCOUT, *who has been flung to the ground, is watching from there. The attacker is not visible.*)

ATTICUS (*as he comes out*): Who called? What is it? Who –

(*Stopping himself as he sees the* MAN *approaching with* JEM. ATTICUS *goes off the porch to help him.*)

ATTICUS: Oh, my God – Jem!

(ATTICUS *helps the* MAN *with* JEM.)

ATTICUS (*calling ahead*): Cal – telephone Doctor Reynolds quick! Tell him *urgent!*

(*The* MAN *is taking* JEM *inside.*)

ATTICUS: Put him down on – (*Turning*) Scout – where's Scout?
SCOUT (*struggling up*): I'm here!

(ATTICUS *rushes to her.*)

SCOUT: I'm all right – the man's gone. But he did somethin' awful to Jem. Atticus – is Jem dead?
ATTICUS (*taking her back to the porch*): He's unconscious. Looks like his arm's broken.

(CALPURNIA *is coming out onto the porch.*)

CALPURNIA: Scout all right?
ATTICUS: Yes.
CALPURNIA: Miss Eula May's getting Doctor Reynolds.
SCOUT (*needing reassurance*): Jem's not dead, is he, Cal?
CALPURNIA: Passed out from the pain. Who did this? Who would –

(ATTICUS *starts to go in with* SCOUT.)

ATTICUS: Call Heck Tate, please. Tell him someone's been after my children.

(*As* ATTICUS *and* SCOUT *go in,* CALPURNIA *turns to stare into the night, involuntarily clenching her fists with outrage. But she is part of a 'lawing family' and she is needed inside. She hurries back in. The light has revealed* JEAN *again.*)

JEAN: After ten forevers, Doctor Reynolds finished with Jem. He said it looked like someone tried to wring his arm off, and it would be a while before Jem could play football again. He added his assurance that Jem was not dead – only under sedation.

(*A man with a flashlight,* HECK TATE, *has come on stage and is approaching the porch.*)

JEAN: Meanwhile Heck Tate had been investigating and when he came to the porch, there was something odd about him.
HECK (*calling*): Atticus –

(ATTICUS *comes onto the porch.*)

ATTICUS: Come in, Heck. Did you find anything? (*Incredulous*) I can't conceive anyone who'd do this.
HECK: Let's stay outside.

(SCOUT *is coming onto the porch as* ATTICUS *steps down to* HECK.)

ATTICUS (*puzzled*): What is it, Heck?
HECK: Bob Ewell's lyin' on the ground yonder with a kitchen knife stuck up under his ribs. He's dead, Mr Finch.

(ATTICUS *is stunned, and* SCOUT *gulps. The* MAN *comes out of the house, standing quietly watching from back by the porch swing.*)

ATTICUS (*bleakly*): Dead? Are you sure?

HECK: Good and dead. He won't hurt these children again.

ATTICUS: But –

HECK (*his anger getting the better of him*): The mean-as-hell, low-down skunk with enough liquor in him to make him brave enough to kill children!

ATTICUS (*in shock*): I thought he'd got it out of him the day he spat at me. And if he hadn't, I thought *I* was the one he'd come after.

HECK: Now you know better. (*To* SCOUT) He broke Jem's arm, and he grabbed you. Then what happened?

SCOUT: Someone came out – to help. Someone –

HECK: Who was it?

SCOUT (*becoming aware of him*): Well, there he is, Mr Tate – he'll tell you his name.

(*They all turn to look at the* MAN *at the back of the porch. He is pale, nervous, withdrawn. As* SCOUT *looks at him, she begins to realise; she takes a step toward him.*)

SCOUT (*gently*): Hey – Boo.

ATTICUS (*to* SCOUT): His right name's Mr Arthur – Boo is just a nickname. Jean Louise, this is Mr Arthur Radley. Maybe you'd like to take him in. You can sit by Jem.

SCOUT: Like to come in, Mr Boo?

(*He nods, takes her arm and they go in.*)

ATTICUS (*turning*): Well, Heck – I guess the thing to do – Jem's a minor, of course. It'll come before county court.

HECK: What will, Mr Finch?

ATTICUS: Of course it's clear-cut self-defence.

HECK: Mr Finch, do you think Jem killed Bob Ewell?

ATTICUS: They were struggling in the dark. He probably got hold of Ewell's knife.

HECK: It wasn't Jem.

ATTICUS: That's kind of you, and I know you're doing it from the good of your heart. But I won't have him grow up with a whisper about him. I won't hush up –

HECK (*sharply*): Hush up what? Jem didn't do it.

ATTICUS: Then who –

HECK (*flatly*): I'll tell you – Bob Ewell fell on his knife. He killed himself.

ATTICUS: Heck, I won't have my children hear me say something different from what they know to be true. If I do, I won't have them any more. I can't live one way in town and another way in my home.

HECK: Mr Finch, I hate to fight you when you're like this. You've been under a strain no man should ever have to go through. Maybe that's why you're not putting two and two together.

ATTICUS (*trying to understand*): If it wasn't Jem –

HECK: Of course it wasn't. His arm was broken.

ATTICUS (*looking toward the porch*): Then it was – it would have to be –

HECK (*emphatically*): Put that thought outa your mind, Mr Finch. I already told you what happened.

(SCOUT *is coming back onto the porch.*)

ATTICUS: But if it was –

HECK: This isn't your decision, Mr Finch, it's all mine. It's my decision, and my responsibility. And there's not much you can do about it.

ATTICUS: What are you saying, Heck?

HECK: I'm saying there's a black man dead for no reason, and the white man responsible for it is dead. So let the dead bury the dead, this time, Mr Finch.

ATTICUS: What about –

HECK: I never heard tell it's against the law for a citizen to do his utmost to prevent a crime from being committed, which is exactly what Boo Radley did. Now maybe you'll say it's my duty to tell the town all about it and not hush it up. Know what'd happen then? All the ladies in Maycomb, including my wife, would be knocking on his door bringing angel food cakes. To my way of thinking, dragging him with his shy ways into the limelight – that's a sin.

(HECK *starts to go, then pauses.*)

HECK: I may not be much, Mr Finch, but I'm still sheriff of Maycomb County, and Bob Ewell fell on his knife. (*Going*) Good night, sir.

(ATTICUS *turns and is surprised to see* SCOUT.)

ATTICUS: Scout.
SCOUT: Yes, Atticus?
ATTICUS: Mr Ewell fell on his knife. Can you possibly understand?
SCOUT: Sir – it looks to me – what Heck said –

(SCOUT *is interrupted by* BOO, *who has come back onto the porch.*)

BOO: Jean Louise?
SCOUT: Yes, Mr Boo?
BOO: Will you take me home?

(SCOUT *nods, offers her arm, and they go toward the Radley house. It is getting much brighter.*)

ATTICUS (*after them*): Arthur –

(SCOUT *and* BOO *pause.*)

ATTICUS: Thank you for my children, Arthur.

(*Then* SCOUT *and* BOO *continue toward the Radley house.*)

JEAN (*quietly*): I remember – the moon had come out – the storm had passed over – and I was being escorted by Boo Radley.

(*They have gone up onto the Radley porch.* BOO *nods, and goes inside.*)

JEAN: He went inside and I never saw him again. But when I turned around, standing on Boo's porch – I saw something else.

(SCOUT *pauses there, looking off.*)

JEAN: A young boy and girl shouting, running to meet their father coming home, the boy going after Mrs Dubose's camellias, the children excited about surprises found in the knothole – and then a stormy night, and those children need him!

(JEAN *turns toward her father, who is waiting for* SCOUT.)

JEAN: Atticus – I was already beginning to stand in other people's shoes! The thing you wanted, Atticus –

(ATTICUS *does not hear.* SCOUT *is running back to him ruefully.*)

JEAN: But – did *you* ever know?
SCOUT (*running up*): Atticus – what Heck Tate said about Boo – about dragging him into the limelight – Heck was right.
ATTICUS: What do you mean?
SCOUT: I mean, it'd be sort of like shooting a mockingbird, wouldn't it?
ATTICUS (*quietly happy*): Yes – yes, it would. Let's go in and sit with Jem.
JEAN (*softly, her lips just forming the words*): You did know.
SCOUT (*as they are going*): All those ideas we had about Boo Radley – But, Atticus – he's real nice.

(*The curtain, if used, is falling. Otherwise the lights are dimming.*)

ATTICUS (*affectionately, as they go in*): Most people are, Scout – when you finally see them.

THE END

Glossary

porch   veranda

sidewalks   pavements

pants   trousers

hooky   truant

scuppernong   a variety of Muscadine grape from which a sweet grape is made. River in North Carolina where it grows.

bulls   head down charge, like a bull

smilax   a climbing plant with greenish or yellow flowers and berry-like fruits

bird dog   hunting dog

druthers   choice, Atticus would rather have used a shotgun

cot   bed

chiffarobe   a chest of drawers for storing clothes, usually with a mirror on the top

sass   impudence

haints   ghosts

Questions and assignments

A Keeping track

A series of questions, Act by Act, for discussion or writing, to keep track of characters, themes and issues as the play progresses.

Students could use these as a basis for a 'journal' of their responses to what they read.

Groups of questions could be used as the basis of a piece of writing for coursework.

Act One

Maycomb

1 (a) What do you learn about the town of Maycomb during the early part of Act One?
(b) How much does the short scene between Atticus and Mr Cunningham tell you about the lives of the people in Maycomb?

The Maycomb way of life

2 (a) 'Manliness' is obviously very important to Scout and Jem at the beginning of the play. What do they think 'manliness' involves?
(b) How does their father, Atticus, not conform to this view?
(c) Later on in Act One, Mrs Dubose criticises Scout for not being 'a lady'. How would most of the people of Maycomb define 'a lady'?
(d) Can you find any evidence in Act One to suggest that

107

the Church is an important part of the lives of the people of Maycomb?

(e) What does Miss Stephanie Crawford's description of family traits tell you about:

   (i) the Maycomb attitude to the past?

   (ii) prejudice in Maycomb?

(f) Is there any connection between the fact that Atticus does not conform to his children's view of 'manliness' and his intention to defend Tom Robinson in the forthcoming trial?

(g) Why does Jem want Atticus to play in the touch football game?

Maycomb people

3 (a) What is Boo Radley's story? What do the people of the town think of him? (Why is he called 'Boo'?)

   (b) What do you learn about Bob and Mayella Ewell from their first brief appearance? (Why do Cal and the Reverend Sykes stop talking when they enter?)

   (c) Why is Dill described by Scout as 'a pocket Merlin'? Why does he, later in Act One, run away from home? Why should he be the one who most wants Boo to come out?

   (d) How do the children see Mrs Dubose? Why does Jem destroy her potted flowers? What is Atticus' response to this incident?

Atticus

4 (a) How much do you learn of Maycomb's view concerning Atticus' forthcoming defence of Tom Robinson?

   (b) Why is Atticus 'startled' when Scout says 'niggers'?

   (c) What is Maycomb's 'usual disease'?

   (d) Why does he say that he is 'licked a hundred years before we started'?

(e) Why does he feel that he *has* to defend Tom Robinson despite the opposition of the town?

(f) What does he mean by 'high talk'? What advice does he give to Scout?

(g) Atticus says: 'We'll be fighting our friends. But remember this, no matter how bitter things get, they're still our friends and this is our home.' Can you explain what he means by this?

Incidents

5 (a) How does the incident with the mad dog alter the children's view of their father? How does Miss Maudie help the children to understand why Atticus had not mentioned his expertise earlier?

(b) Describe the incident which takes place outside the jailhouse. How does Scout alter the situation? What is Atticus' response?

(c) What is the case against Tom Robinson – as described by Heck Tate and Bob Ewell at the beginning of the trial?

The mockingbird

6 (a) What does Atticus tell the children about the mockingbird?

(b) At this stage, can you see any connection between the mockingbird, Boo Radley and Tom Robinson?

Act Two

The prosecution

1 (a) How does Atticus undermine the testimonies of Bob Ewell and Mayella?

(b) What do Bob Ewell and Mayella reveal about themselves in the way they give their evidence?

(c) How does Mr Gilmore treat Tom Robinson during the trial?

(d) Which aspect of Tom's evidence does Mr Gilmore highlight in trying to turn the jury against Tom

The defence

2 (a) Look closely at what Tom Robinson says and the way in which he gives his evidence:
   (i) Why did he help Mayella?
  (ii) What really happened to Mayella?
 (iii) Why will he not repeat Bob Ewell's language?
 (iv) Why does he say that Mayella was 'mistaken in her mind', not that she is lying?
  (v) How would you describe Tom's manner during questioning?

(b) What are Atticus' main points in his summing up – about the real 'crime', about the black community and about equality and the law?

The onlookers

3 (a) Where do the children sit during the trial? Is this important?

(b) Why does Dill cry?

(c) Jem is sure that Tom will be freed. Why?

(d) Comment on the behaviour of Helen Robinson and the Reverend Sykes during the trial.

(e) Why does Bob Ewell spit in Atticus' face shortly after the evidence has been given?

The verdict

4 Describe the reactions of the following people to the verdict:
   Jem

Taking an angle

Calpurnia ~~Treats children individuals no predjudice, calphurnia~~
Atticus
Dill (why does he say 'I'll become a clown'?)
Bob Ewell
Miss Stephanie Crawford
Miss Maudie (how does Miss Maudie help the children
to cope with the defeat?)

'Suddenly death was among us'

5 (a) After the death of Mrs Dubose, Atticus tells Jem that
    there was something he wanted him to see. What was it?
    (b) Why did Tom try to escape?
    (c) Describe the death of Bob Ewell.

The play's conclusion ~~He knows case is lost befoe started.~~

6 (a) Why does Heck Tate insist that Arthur Radley's part in
    the death of Bob Ewell be kept secret?
    (b) 'To stand in other people's shoes'. What does this
    mean – what attitude is the play promoting?
    (c) How is the community's treatment of Tom Robinson
    and Arthur Radley like the 'sin' of killing a mockingbird?
    (d) Do you find the ending hopeful or not?

B Taking an angle

Looking at the play from different angles and writing in different forms.

1 Imagine that, in later years, Dill writes to Scout. Write his
letter, in which he describes why he preferred being with her
family rather than his own: he tells her why he was unhappy
in his own home; what her family gave him; why he felt a
particular sympathy for Boo Radley and why he tended to
exaggerate things to her and Jem. Most importantly, he tells

Scout how the trial of Tom Robinson has remained with him in later life: why he was less able to cope at the time and why he found it so hard to come to terms with the injustice of it in later life.

2 Write (or improvise) the scene in which Bob Ewell tells Mayella what she has to say at the trial.

3 Write a poem called 'The Death of Tom Robinson'.

4 Improvise (or write an account of) the jury's discussion after hearing the evidence at the trial. How do they justify their verdict to each other?

5 As a group discuss the idea of 'manliness' as it is explored in the play. (What do the children think it is at the beginning. How and why do their views change?) What is the play saying 'courage' really is?

6 Atticus goes to see Mayella after the death of her father. What do they say to each other? Has Mayella changed? How does Atticus convince her that he does not dislike her?

7 Write a letter (from yourself) to Helen Robinson in which you try to comfort her and explain to her that Tom's death was not a complete waste.

8 Write (or role-play) an interview given by a newspaper reporter with Walter Cunningham. He is being asked about the events of the night during which he went with a mob to the jailhouse. Why did he go? What happened? Why did he 'back off'? What has he learned about how a mob works and how a mob can change its mind?

9 In groups make a list of the ways in which *loneliness* is an important theme in the play. When you have made your list, see if you can identify what the play is saying *makes* people lonely – what keeps people apart from each other. (In other words, who is lonely in the play, and why has their society made them lonely?)

10 Design a cover or a poster for the play – a picture which you think illustrates the idea of killing a mockingbird (and perhaps the relationship between this image and Tom Robinson/Boo Radley.

C Extended assignments

Larger, more detailed coursework assignments.

1   Put together a complete front page of the Maycomb week-ly newspaper, *The Maycomb Tribune*, reporting the trial of Tom Robinson. You might consider the following elements for in-clusion: the headline and lead story; an 'exclusive' interview with one of the participants; editorial comment; an advertise-ment; other (brief) news. (Note: the date would be during the summer of 1935.)

Decide whether *The Maycomb Tribune* is a 'popular' news-paper or a 'quality' newspaper. Look at different newspapers to see how the layout, emphasis, headlining and language would be different in each case.

2   Read the novel and compare it with the play. Write a letter from Harper Lee (the novelist) to Christopher Sergel (the dra-matist) in which she says what she thinks of his adaptation. (She may complain about what he has left out, e.g. various minor characters and incidents such as the visit to Cal's church and the burning of Miss Maudie's house – as well as Scout's experiences at school.) In her letter, Harper Lee should give examples and say why she thinks these things are important. Following this you might write a reply from Christopher Sergel in which he explains his omissions and says what his main intentions were in writing his play.

D   Essay titles

Subjects for literary appreciation.

1   'You can't repeat the past.'
    'Can't repeat the past?' he cried incredulously. 'Why of course you can!'
        (F. Scott Fitzgerald, *The Great Gatsby*)

'. . . we were licked a hundred years before we started . . .'
(Atticus in *To Kill a Mockingbird*)
How does the past dominate the events of the play? How far
does Atticus overcome this domination?

2   Discuss the presentation of the black characters in the
play, *To Kill a Mockingbird*.

3   In the novel, there is a character called Mr Raymond who
appears briefly during the trial sitting with Scout, Jem and
Dill. When Dill cries, Mr Raymond understands why: 'Cry
about the simple hell people give other people – without even
thinking. Cry about the hell white people give coloured folks,
without even stopping to think that they're people too.'
(Chapter 20). Does cruelty 'win' in the play?

4   'The children's unreasoning fear of the eccentric is
obliquely compared to the community's hatred of the black.
Both Robinson and Radley are symbolised by the mockingbird
that it is a 'sin to kill'; both are feared because unknown.'
Discuss the image of the mockingbird and its relation to Tom
Robinson and Arthur Radley.

5   What is Atticus teaching his children as they grow up,
and how does he do it?

6   How important is family life as a theme in the play, *To Kill
a Mockingbird*?

7   Give an account of Tom Robinson's trial showing Atticus'
skill in defending Tom and explaining why the defence fails.

8   How does Arthur Radley help the children? What do they
give him in return?

9   Describe and explain Atticus' feelings towards the people
of Maycomb.

10   Consider the importance of the following characters in
the play:

   Dill

   Miss Maudie

   Mrs Dubose

11   How is the play, *To Kill a Mockingbird* different from the
novel? How much is the detail altered? Is the emphasis

changed? Is the final impact the same? Which do you prefer and why?

12 Compare the play, *To Kill a Mockingbird* with any other novel or play which you have read on a similar theme or themes.

E Further reading

There are a number of American novels which you may find interesting to read alongside this play.

For the work of another woman writing about the 'deep south' and dealing with the theme of isolation, see:

Carson McCullers,   *The Heart is a Lonely Hunter,*
                     Member of the Wedding.

Works of black American writers which you might find rewarding include:

Maya Angelou,   *I know why the caged bird sings;*
James Baldwin,   *Go Tell it on the Mountain;*
Alice Walker,   *The Color Purple;*
Richard Wright, *Black Boy.*

Look also at some of the recent novels written for people of your age:

Kristin Hunter, *The Soul Brothers and Sister Lou;*
Julius Lester,   *Long Journey Home;*
                 Basket Ball Player.

Also recommended are the novels of Mildred Taylor and Rosa Guy.

Atticus is fair. He tells Scout that 'until you climb into someone elses skin' then you should not judge people (P15).

He may seem boring because he doesn't join in the game of football P 17.

He knows that he has lost the case of defending Tom Robinson but he still takes on the job.

He treats his children as individuals, grown ups by letting them call him Atticus & not Dad.

When someone has a debt to pay to him if they are poor he will let them pay in ways which they are able. (P16)

He does not boost about his talents e.g 'Being the deadest shot in Maycombe'. He doesn't even tell his children.

They became proud of their father again when they see him shoot the dog. P29.

...e doesn't believe in violence
even sits outside the jail
defend Tom against the lynch
mob without a gun. Just a
chair & newspaper. P 44.

He only becomes scared when
cat appears. He is not
scared for himself but for
cat. P45

When in court room he keeps
jury out for a long time.
All the coloured people stand
to pay their respect to
Atticus.

He is prepared to send Jem
through all the channels when he
thinks he has killed Bob Ewell
He makes no allowances for
him (102)